Isn't it funny when...
Que c'est drôle quand...

219 Stories by Canadian Children

219 nouvelles par des jeunes Canadiens

STAPLES
Business DEPOT

that was easy.™

BUREAU
EN GROS

rien de plus simple.ᴹᶜ

It is our pleasure to donate all net proceeds
from the sale of this book to Canadian schools.

Nous sommes heureux de pouvoir faire don de toutes les recettes
nettes provenant de la vente de ce livre à des écoles canadiennes.

1

Published by/Publié par

**The Business Depot Ltd.
30 Centurian Drive, Suite 106
Markham, Ontario, L3R 8B9**

Find us on the World Wide Web at: **staples.ca or bureauengros.com**
Nous nous trouvons sur le Web à : **bureauengros.com ou staples.ca**

STAPLES Business Depot/ BUREAU EN GROS will donate all net proceeds from book sales for even distribution among over 200 of the Canadian schools with students submitting entries, selected by draw. Additionally, $5,000.00 in gift cards will be presented to the school of our First-Prize winner.

STAPLES Business Depot/ BUREAU EN GROS fera don de toutes les recettes nettes provenant des ventes de ce livre en les distribuant équitablement entre plus de 200 écoles des étudiants participants, choisies par tirage. De plus, 5 000 $ en cartes-cadeaux sera offert à l'école du gagnant du premier prix.

For further details of donations contributed to schools by STAPLES Business Depot/BUREAU EN GROS, please write to:

Pour de plus amples détails concernant les dons faits aux écoles par STAPLES Business Depot/BUREAU EN GROS, veuillez écrire à :

P.O. Box 3619 Industrial Park, Markham, ON, L3R 9Z9

Cover design/conception de la couverture : Isabelle Tremblay
Cover illustration/illustration de la couverture : RoseMarie Condon
First imprint/première date de publication: November/novembre 2003
ISBN 0-9689688-3-X
Printed and bound in Canada   Imprimé et relié au Canada

Acknowledgements

STAPLES Business Depot/BUREAU EN GROS would like to thank the following organizations and individuals for their efforts in making this book possible:

- Kenneth Oppel
- RoseMarie Condon
- Hewlett Packard for their generous prize donations of a computer and a digital camera.
- The Delta Group, for their printing contributions.
- The thousands of children from across Canada who entered the challenge. Without their submissions, we would not have been able to compile such an outstanding anthology of stories.
- All the STAPLES Business Depot/BUREAU EN GROS associates who supported this project by donating their time to serve as judges and perform administrative duties.

And... a big Thank You to all of you who have contributed toward the education of Canadian children by purchasing this book!

Remerciements

STAPLES Business Depot/BUREAU EN GROS aimerait remercier les organisations et personnes suivantes pour les efforts fournis pour réaliser ce livre :

- Kenneth Oppel
- RoseMarie Condon
- Hewlett Packard pour leur don généreux d'un ordinateur et d'un appareil photo numérique.
- Le Delta Group pour sa contribution à l'impression de ce livre.
- Les milliers d'enfants dans tout le Canada qui ont participé au concours. Sans eux, nous ne pourrions compiler cette extraordinaire anthologie de nouvelles.
- Tous les associés de STAPLES Business Depot/BUREAU EN GROS qui ont aidé à ce projet en donnant leur temps pour servir comme juges préliminaires et effectuer les tâches administratives.

Et... un grand merci à vous tous qui avez contribué à l'éducation des enfants canadiens en achetant ce livre !

Foreword by

Steve Matyas,
President,
STAPLES Business Depot/
BUREAU EN GROS

It is my pleasure to welcome you to our third annual national writing challenge for children.

I'm reminded of the adage that in choosing to take even the smallest of actions, each and every one of us has the power to influence the state of this world and make it a better place. In 2001, we chose to champion the value of literacy by providing a forum for our young people to unleash their imaginations, have fun writing creatively, and gain rewards for their efforts. The results far surpassed our expectations. Not only were a huge number of young people inspired to write and submit stories, but, as well, there was plenty of evidence to prove that Canada will be enjoying a whole new crop of award-winning authors in the future!

In a nutshell, every ounce of encouragement provided today could make all the difference to a child's tomorrow. Congratulations to all the young people who submitted stories. Keep writing, give your imagination free rein, and feed your dreams.

Thank you,

4

J'ai le plaisir de vous accueillir à notre troisième concours d'écriture annuel à l'échelle nationale destiné aux enfants.

Je me rappelle de l'adage selon lequel toute action, même petite, donne à chacun de nous le pouvoir d'influencer le monde et de le rendre meilleur. En 2001, nous avons choisi de patronner l'alphabétisme en offrant à nos jeunes une tribune pour donner libre cours à leur imagination, pour qu'ils s'amusent en écrivant d'une façon créative et pour les récompenser de leurs efforts. Les résultats ont de loin dépassé nos attentes. Non seulement un grand nombre de jeunes ont été inspirés pour écrire et envoyer leur histoire, mais nous pouvons aussi prouver avec certitude que le Canada jouira, à l'avenir, d'une nouvelle génération de jeunes auteurs primés !

En un mot, chaque brin d'encouragement offert aujourd'hui pourrait faire toute la différence dans la vie d'un enfant. Félicitations à tous les jeunes qui ont envoyé leur histoire. Continuez à écrire, ne freinez pas votre imagination et nourrissez vos rêves.

Merci.

SMatyas

Préface par

Steve Matyas,
Président,
STAPLES Business Depot/
BUREAU EN GROS

Foreword by

Kenneth Oppel,
Children's Book Author

Starting a story is one the hardest parts of writing. You want your first sentence to be perfect. You want to grab the reader's attention, and make him or her desperate to read the second sentence, and the third and the fourth...

Every time you start writing, you're starting with nothing but a blank piece of paper (or a blank computer screen) and the ideas banging around in your head. You've got a whole world in there. Absolutely anything could happen. And it's all up to you. You have to make the decisions. Sometimes, when I'm writing, I wish someone would just give me the first sentence. Surely it would make things easier! At least it would give me a starting point. But it also forces you to think about a specific idea – one that you might not have cared to think about before. It's hard work. For instance, I've been staring at the phrase, "Isn't it funny when..." for about half an hour now, and I haven't had a single idea.

If I've learned anything in my years of writing, it's that there are no rules, just choices. Should my hero go down the dark corridor? Or just run back home, jump into bed, and pull the sheets over his head? What's important is choosing a path and seeing where it takes you. And that will usually show you if you've made the right decision. The great thing about writing is that you can always go back and change things. So just jump in. Don't worry about making mistakes and wrong turns. Eventually, you're bound to end up somewhere interesting.

Commencer une histoire est l'une des choses les plus difficiles de l'écriture. Vous voulez que votre première phrase soit parfaite. Vous voulez attirer l'attention du lecteur et l'obliger à lire la deuxième phrase, et la troisième et la quatrième...

Chaque fois que vous commencez à écrire, vous commencez avec rien qu'un morceau de papier vierge (ou un écran d'ordinateur vide) et des idées plein la tête. Vous avez là tout un monde où tout peut arriver et cela ne dépend que de vous. C'est à vous de décider. Parfois, lorsque j'écris, je souhaite que quelqu'un me donne la première phrase. Cela rendrait sûrement les choses plus faciles ! J'aurais au moins un point de départ. Mais cela vous force à penser à une idée précise – une chose à laquelle vous n'aviez peut-être pas pensé auparavant. C'est un travail dur. Par exemple, je regarde la phrase « Que c'est drôle quand... » voici maintenant plus d'une demi-heure et aucune idée ne m'est venue.

Si j'ai appris quelque chose de mes années d'écriture, c'est qu'il n'y a aucune règle, il n'y a que des choix. Mon héros devrait-il emprunter le sombre couloir ? Ou juste rentrer en courant à la maison, aller au lit et cacher sa tête sous les draps ? L'important est de choisir un passage et de voir où il débouchera. Et vous saurez si vous avez pris la bonne décision. Ce qui est intéressant dans l'écriture, c'est que vous pouvez toujours faire marche arrière et changer les choses. Alors, n'hésitez pas. Ne vous inquiétez pas de commettre des erreurs. Tôt ou tard, vous finirez par arriver quelque part d'intéressant.

Préface par

**Kenneth Oppel,
auteur de livres d'enfants**

Kenneth Oppel

Kenneth Oppel wrote his first book, Colin's Fantastic Video Adventure, during his summer holidays when he was fourteen, and addicted to video games. With his parents' help, he submitted his book to a number of Canadian publishers, all of whom rejected it. The next summer, Kenneth rewrote his story, expanding and improving it. He then sent it to his favourite author, Roald Dahl. Dahl was kind enough to read the book, and recommend it to his own literary agent, and the book was published in 1985. Since then, Kenneth has written numerous books for children and young adults, including Silverwing, Sunwing and Firewing. An animated TV series of Silverwing is airing this fall on Teletoon.

Kenneth was born in Port Alberni, British Columbia, and spent most of his childhood in Victoria, and on the opposite coast, in Halifax. He studied English and Cinema at the University of Toronto and has lived and worked in Oxford, Corner Brook, Newfoundland, and Dublin. He now lives in Toronto with his wife and two children.

This coming spring will see the publication of his new fantasy novel, Airborn, set in an imagined past when giant airships ruled the skies.

To learn more about Kenneth, visit his website at:
www.kennethoppel.com

On behalf of Kenneth Oppel, a donation has been made to UNICEF, a charity of his choice, for his contribution to this year's Writing Challenge.

Isn't it funny when you tell a joke, and nobody laughs, and then someone else tells exactly the same joke ten minutes later and everyone kills themselves laughing? Happens to me all the time. I'm the worst joke teller in the world. I'd mangle anything. But my older sister can make even the lamest joke funny. It's all in the way she tells it. I've studied her. I've taken notes. I've tried to copy her. But it's no good. Don't sweat it, she says to me. Try something else. Maybe she's right. Maybe I'm just a different kind of storyteller.

Kenneth Oppel, Toronto

Kenneth Oppel a écrit son premier livre, Colin's Fantastic Video Adventure, durant ses vacances d'été, à quatorze ans, lorsqu'il était un mordu des jeux vidéo. Avec l'aide de ses parents, il a envoyé son livre à plusieurs éditeurs canadiens qui l'ont rejeté. L'été suivant, Kenneth a réécrit son histoire en la développant et en l'améliorant. Il l'a envoyé alors à son auteur préféré, qui, après l'avoir lue, l'a recommandée à son propre agent littéraire. Le livre a été publié en 1985. Depuis lors, Kenneth a écrit de nombreux livres pour enfants et jeunes adultes, y compris Silverwing, Sunwing et Firewing. Les séries de dessins animés Silverwing seront diffusées en automne sur Teletoon.

Kenneth est né à Port Alberni en Colombie-Britannique et a passé la grande partie de son enfance à Victoria et sur la côte opposée, à Halifax. Il a étudié l'anglais et le cinéma à l'université de Toronto. Il a vécu et travaillé à Oxford, à Corner Brook, à Terre-Neuve et à Dublin. Actuellement, il vit à Toronto avec sa femme et ses deux enfants.

Au prochain printemps, nous verrons la publication de son nouveau roman fantastique, Airborn, se déroulant dans un passé imaginaire quand les engins spatiaux gigantesques dominaient les cieux.

Pour en savoir plus au sujet de Kenneth, visitez son site web à : www.kennethoppel.com

Au nom de Kenneth Oppel, un don a été fait à l'UNICEF, organisation charitable de son choix, pour sa contribution au concours d'écriture de cette année.

Kenneth Oppel

Que c'est drôle quand une anecdote racontée par vous ne fasse rire personne et que la même anecdote racontée par une autre personne dix minutes plus tard fasse rire aux larmes tout le monde. Cela m'arrive tout le temps. Il n'y a pas pire que moi pour raconter des anecdotes. Je rate tout. Mais ma sœur aînée peut rendre amusante l'anecdote la plus fade. C'est sa façon de raconter. Je l'ai étudiée. J'ai pris des notes. J'ai essayé de la copier. Mais en vain. Calme-toi, me disait-elle. Essaie quelque chose d'autre. Peut-être qu'elle a raison. Peut-être que je suis un raconteur différent d'histoires.

Kenneth Oppel, Toronto

1

FIRST PLACE
PREMIÈRE PLACE

Michelle Vandermoor
Age 12, Maple Ridge, BC,
Whonnock Elementary School

Illustrated by/Illustration par RoseMarie Condon

Isnt it funny when, you wake up at night. You stretch, yawn, flick on the light. You lift up the covers, slip out of bed, tiptoe downstairs not a word, nothing said. And for no particular reason when you get to the bottom, you open the door to that cold night in Autumn. You step to the grass excitement grow'n, you feel the wind it's really blow'n. You stare at the sky for something new, all you see is stars looking at you. So you go back to bed, turn off the light, maybe there'll be something more the next night.

Michelle Vandermoor age 12.

Isn't it funny when you wake up at night, you stretch, yawn, flick on the light. You lift up the covers, slip out of bed, tiptoe downstairs, not a word, nothing said. And for no particular reason, when you reach the bottom, you open the door to that cold night in Autumn; you step to the grass, excitement growing, you feel the wind, it's really blowing. You stare at the sky for something new, all you see is stars looking at you. So you go back to bed, turn off the light, maybe there will be something more the next night.

Michelle Vandermoor, Age 12, Maple Ridge, BC
Whonnock Elementary School

Que c'est drôle quand... Je vois les fleurs de ma mère se balancer de tous les côtés, on dirait qu'elles dansent avec le rythme du vent. On dirait que le vent est la musique et que les fleurs sont les danseurs. Juste en les regardant, j'ai envie de danser comme les fleurs et de chanter avec le vent. Peu importe la mélodie du vent, qu'il soit doux ou violent, les fleurs ont toujours plaisir à suivre son rythme. De plus si ils ont le bonheur d'avoir la lumière du soleil, cela deviendra SUBLIME!

Marie-Gaëlle Grenier 10 ans

Que c'est drôle quand je vois les fleurs de ma mère se balancer de tous les côtés, on dirait qu'elles dansent avec le rythme du vent. On dirait que le vent est la musique et que les fleurs sont les danseurs. Juste en les regardant, j'ai envie de danser comme les fleurs et de chanter avec le vent. Peu importe la mélodie du vent, qu'il soit doux ou violent, les fleurs ont toujours plaisir à suivre son rythme. De plus, s'ils ont le bonheur d'avoir la lumière du soleil, cela deviendra SUBLIME !

SECOND PLACE/DEUXIÈME PLACE

Marie-Gaëlle Grenier, 10 ans, St-Germain, QC
École Roméo Salois

Isn't it funny when your pet dragon sneezes? A baby dragon's sneeze is a little grey puff of smoke, no harm done you'll just cough or possibly choke. A full grown dragon's sneeze is mostly red and orange flames. These flames can reach up to three metres. So, it is best to keep your pet dragon free from colds or flu. I suggest an inoculation and an appointment with an allergist wouldn't hurt too. Keep your dragon healthy whatever you do. Free from sniffles and sneezes or else you might find yourself a little roasted or even worse completely toasted!

Kelsey MacEachern age-9

Isn't it funny when your pet dragon sneezes? A baby dragon's sneeze is a little grey puff of smoke; no harm done, you'll just cough or possibly choke. A full grown dragon's sneeze is mostly red and orange flames. These flames can reach up to three metres. So, it is best to keep your pet dragon free from colds or flu. I suggest an inoculation and an appointment with an allergist wouldn't hurt too. Keep your dragon healthy whatever you do. Free from sniffles and sneezes or else you might find yourself a little roasted, or even worse, completely toasted!

THIRD PLACE/TROISIÈME PLACE

Kelsey MacEachern, Age 9, Brantford, ON
Briar Park Public School

13

Isn't it funny when your little sister complains about monsters under the bed? Hopefully her monster is as nice as mine. Every night I shrink myself to the size of a peanut and go exploring under my bed. I go around last week's lunch, through my dirty gym socks, and over my dog's discarded bone. Then, I look behind my overdue homework to see a big, green, hairy monster that I call, "Google-snooze." I visit him because he gets lonely and needs me for a friend. Yep, that's my Google-snooze. I visit him every night, In my dreams.

Veronica Allan   13

Isn't it funny when your little sister complains about monsters under the bed? Hopefully, her monster is as nice as mine. Every night I shrink myself to the size of a peanut and go exploring under my bed. I go around last week's lunch, through my dirty gym socks and over my dog's discarded bone. Then I look behind my overdue homework to see a big, green, hairy monster that I call 'Google-Snooze'. I visit him because he gets lonely and needs me for a friend. Yep, that's my Google-Snooze. I visit him every night, in my dreams.

Veronica Allan, Age 13, Shallow Lake, ON
Hillcrest Elementary School

Isn't it funny when you mix up your family's Christmas presents? It was the day before Christmas and I just finished wrapping my family's presents. I went downstairs, put the presents under the tree, and went to bed. The next morning I raced downstairs and we each opened a present. Each member of my family opened the present I gave them. My sister got a tie, my brother got a hairdryer, my mum got a baseball bat, and my dad got a dollhouse. "I mixed up the presents!" I told them. "That's okay," they said, "we'll find uses for them."

Kelsey Allen, 13

Isn't it funny when you mix up your family's Christmas presents? It was the day before Christmas and I just finished wrapping my family's presents. I went downstairs, put the presents under the tree, and went to bed. The next morning, I raced downstairs and we each opened a present. Each member of my family opened the present I gave them. My sister got a tie, my brother got a hairdryer, my mum got a baseball bat, and my dad got a dollhouse. "I mixed up the presents!" I told them. "That's okay," they said, "we'll find uses for them."

Kelsey Allen, Age 13, North Vancouver, BC
Handsworth Secondary

Isn't it funny when giants sneeze and blow everything away except for one little dandelion. It has happened once at my Uncle's cottage. A huge wind came through and knocked over trees and everything but some little tiny planters sitting empty on their deck. What I am trying to say is that even the smallest thing can make a huge difference in the world. Let's not ignore the small and make fun of them, let's accept them. You never know, someday they might make a huge difference in the world.

Bryan ambrose, 11

Isn't it funny when giants sneeze and blow everything away except for one little dandelion? It has happened once at my uncle's cottage. A huge wind came through and knocked over trees and everything but some little tiny planters sitting empty on their deck. What I am trying to say is that even the smallest thing can make a huge difference in the world. Let's not ignore the small and make fun of them, let's accept them. You never know, someday they might make a huge difference in the world.

Bryan Ambrose, Age 11, Waterloo, ON
K.W. Bilingual School

Isn't it Funny When....................
Isn't it funny when birds climb trees and
elephants step on bees or when spider are
right beside us.
Isn't it funny when dogs and eats are
freaky of bats, or when we wear funny hats then
get dusty mats.
Isn't it funny when we drink coke
and spit it out then we are soaked or when
we get so lazy than so crazy.
Isn't it funny when we get so scared
when we get dared or when we look up at
the moon than day-light comes so soon.
Isn't it Funny When....................

Andrea Andersen Age 12

Isn't it funny when birds climb trees and elephants step on bees, or when spiders are right beside us. Isn't it funny when dogs and cats are freaky of bats, or when we wear funny hats then we have dusty mats. Isn't it funny when we drink coke and spit it out, then we are soaked, or when we get so lazy, then so crazy. Isn't it funny when we get so scared when we get dared, or when we look up at the moon, then daylight comes so soon. Isn't it funny when….

Andrea Andersen, Age 12, Makkovik, Lab.
John Christian Erhardt Memorial

The Gypsy in my Eye

Isn't it funny when dreams come true? That happened to me, and you won't believe what occurred! I dreamt that I made a model unicorn which became real! She told me that her name was Gypsy. They say that you could catch a unicorn with gold but my hair was the only gold I had, so I ripped a piece out and tied it onto her. It worked but you and I know that if you love something, let it go. I was fond of her but she was homesick, so I said goodbye to the gypsy in my eye.

Kaila Anderson, 11

Isn't it funny when dreams come true? That happened to me, and you won't believe what occurred! I dreamt that I made a model unicorn, which became real! She told me that her name was Gypsy. They say that you could catch a unicorn with gold, but my hair was the only gold I had, so I ripped a piece out and tied it onto her. It worked, but you and I know that if you love something, let it go. I was fond of her but she was homesick, so I said goodbye to the Gypsy in my eye.

Kaila Anderson, Age 11, Scarborough, ON
Hunter's Glen Jr. Public School

Isn't it funny when you wake up on the wrong side of the bed your day is ruined. My problem is I don't know which side is the wrong side. My bed has a left side and a right side but where is the wrong side? If I always get out of the bed on the right side, will I always have good days? My bed is against a wall so I can only get out on one side. So why is it some days it's the right side and some days it's the wrong side?

Autumn Bailey Age 8

Isn't it funny when you wake up on the wrong side of the bed and your day is ruined. My problem is I don't know which side is the wrong side. My bed has a left side and a right side but where is the wrong side? If I always get out of the bed on the right side, will I always have good days? My bed is against a wall, so I can only get out on one side. So why is it some days it's the right side and some days it's the wrong side?

Autumn Bailey, Age 8, Burlington, ON
St. John's School

Isn't it funny when you live in the ground?
It's icky and sticky, you act like a hound!
You start to eat spiders and yucky old worms,
But whenever you have some, you get others' germs!
You live in a house made from mud and dry grass,
But the one good thing is, that you have not one class!
But I'm glad I'm not there and I don't want to be,
I'm happy and jolly and normal you see!
I like it up here 'cause you learn all the time,
And 'cause you can always just makeup a rhyme!

by: Lia Baird Age 9

Isn't it funny when you live in the ground? It's icky and sticky, you act like a hound! You start to eat spiders and yucky old worms, but whenever you have some, you get others' germs! You live in a house made from mud and dry grass, but the one good thing is, that you have not one class! But I'm glad I'm not there and I don't want to be. I'm happy and jolly and normal you see! I like it up here 'cause you learn all the time, and 'cause you can always just make up a rhyme!

Lia Baird, Age 9, Thornhill, ON
U.S.D.S. (Bayview Campus)

Isn't it funny when you find false teeth in your gym bag? My friends all laughed. I didn't. Granddad was my favorite. He taught me card tricks, and read me Robbie Burn's poems. Now his ashes are over the ocean. Nothing remains of him, apart from his false teeth. I remembered playing "Find my Falsies" with him, and I remembered the time I couldn't find them. The best "Find my Falsies" player had forgotten where he had hidden them. I blamed Alzheimer's. A year later, finding false teeth in your gym bag can be not only funny, but also sad.

David Balcarras, 13

Isn't it funny when you find false teeth in your gym bag?
My friends all laughed. I didn't. Granddad was my favorite.
He taught me card tricks, and read me Robbie Burns' poems.
Now his ashes are over the ocean. Nothing remains of him,
apart from his false teeth. I remember playing 'Find my Falsies'
with him, and I remember the time I couldn't find them. The best
'Find my Falsies' player had forgotten where he had hidden
them. I blamed Alzheimer's. A year later, finding false teeth
in your gym bag can be not only funny, but also sad.

David Balcarras, Age 13, Oshawa, ON
Pierre Elliott Trudeau Public School

Isn't it funny when you fall on your face? Isn't if wonderful
to win a long race? Isn't it scary to disappear without a trace?
Isn't it cool to go into space? Isn't it fun to see a new place,
and isn't it nice to have a dinner of rice? Isn't it bad to have
a few lice? Isn't it interesting to watch some white mice?
Isn't it good to skate on thin ice? Isn't it neat to try a new
spice, and do you have answers to questions like these?
I have, but you can do as you please.

Meaghan Ballard, Age 11, Winnipeg, MB
Charleswood Junior High

Que c'est drôle quand le soir dans ma chambre je retrouve mon univers. Il y a des habitants des petits et des grands. Chacun d'eux a un nom et une personalité, comme dans notre monde quoi! Sauf que dans cet univers il n'y à pas de guerres et tout le monde se fait confiance. C'est un monde remplis de bonheur et d'amour. Même si les habitants sont muets ils parlent avec leurs coeurs. Leurs âmes sont si pures qu'ils ne peuvent pas mentir. Vous deviez vous en doutez ses habitants sont bien et bel des toutous qu'on emmène partout partout!

♡   ♡   ♡   ♡   ♡ ♡

Eva-Ana Barroso Riccardi 10 ans

Que c'est drôle quand le soir dans ma chambre, je retrouve mon univers. Il y a des habitants, des petits et des grands. Chacun d'eux a un nom et une personnalité, comme dans notre monde, quoi ! Sauf que, dans cet univers, il n'y a pas de guerre et tout le monde se fait confiance. C'est un monde rempli de bonheur et d'amour. Même si les habitants sont muets, ils parlent avec leurs coeurs. Leur âme est si pure qu'ils ne peuvent pas mentir. Vous deviez vous en douter, ses habitants sont bel et bien des toutous qu'on emmène partout, partout !

**Eva-Ana Barroso Riccardi, 10 ans,
Montréal, QC, École Nesbitt**

Que c'est drôle quand j'ai fait mon curieux
dans la cuisine. J'ai décidé de jeter un coup
d'oeil dans le bol sur le comptoir. Je n'y
arrivais pas. Alors j'ai sauté, mais je n'ai pas
réussi. Alors, j'ai eu une idée : j'ai pris une

chaise. Je suis arrivé à peine à toucher le bol. Par accident,
j'ai versé le bol sur ma tête. Je suis sorti de la cuisine avec
beaucoup de farine sur moi. Ma grand-mère a aperçu le bol
par terre et elle a commencé à rire en me voyant.
J'avais l'air d'un fantôme.

Julien Bejjani, 9 ans, Ottawa, ON
École International L'Odyssée

Isn't it funny, when dogs walk people On leashes. Well, a long time ago there Was a town. Then One day an Evil Emperor came and hid in a hotel. While he Was in the hotel he thought of a scheme to rule the world. His scheme was to turn people into dogs. So he went to his lab and made a spell. Then he pretended that it Was lemon ade. Then everyone turned into dogs But one girl didn't have the drink and she turned everyone back. Then she locked him up Then everyone was happy. The end.

Madeline Berger Age 8

Isn't it funny when dogs walk people on leashes? Well, a long time ago there was a town. Then one day an Evil Emperor came and hid in a hotel. While he was in the hotel, he thought of a scheme to rule the world. His scheme was to turn people into dogs. So he went to his lab and made a spell. Then he pretended that it was lemonade. Then everybody turned into dogs, but then one girl didn't have the drink and she turned everyone back. Then she locked him up! Then everyone was so happy! The End

Madeline Berger, Age 8, Langley, BC
Nicomekl School

Isn't it funny when a Ketten purrs? The way she sleeps ever so quietly on a white window sill, decorated elegantly with whitelaced curtains, and the warm, soothing sunlight shining in though the the oak trees outside. Suddenly the light, grey, soft Ketten begins her purr and breaks the still silence. Her whiskers twitch everytime she breaths softly to continue her beautiful song from inside. Her happy symphony sounds like two rolling balls that hit everytime she moves. Her long fluffy tail sways to the rhythm. Then, her long beautiful chant ends as she enters another wonderful dream ending her day. Whitney .T. Bettis age .13

Isn't it funny when a kitten purrs? The way she sleeps ever so quietly on a white window sill, decorated elegantly with white lace curtains, and the warm soothing sunlight shining in through the oak trees outside. Suddenly, the light grey, soft kitten begins her purr and breaks the still silence. Her whiskers twitch every time she breathes softly to continue her beautiful song from inside. Her happy symphony sounds like two rolling balls that hit every time she moves. Her long, fluffy tail sways to the rhythm. Then, her long, beautiful chant ends as she enters another wonderful dream ending her day.

Whitney T. Bettis, Age 13, Cornwall, ON
St. Peter's School

Isn't it funny when something unexpected happens and you weren't ready for it? Well one day, I found a giant egg. It was bigger than a car! I only told my sister about it after she had promised not to tell anyone else. We left it outside in the sun all day long while we were at school. When we came home, there was an omelette left in its place. We were very surprised. We went inside to find some green peppers, mushrooms and other stuff, then we threw it all into the omelette and had a great big feast.

Caitlin. Blaedow   11 (Age)

Isn't it funny when something unexpected happens and you weren't ready for it? Well, one time, I found a giant egg. It was bigger than a car! I told only my sister about it after she had promised not to tell anybody about it. We left it out in the sun all day long while we went to school. When we came home, there was an omelette left in its place. We were very surprised. We went inside and found some green peppers and other stuff, then we threw it all onto the omelette and had a great big feast.

Caitlin Blaedow, Age 11, Frankville, ON
Frankville Public School

Que c'est drôle quand je m'imagine en train
de me baigner dans un lac rempli de
fruits. Et puis j'embarquais sur une
chenille géante. Nous flottions tranquillement quand une grosse grenouille
voulait nous manger. Heureusement, un
lutin se trouvait près du lac et avec
son filet magique, il nous attrapais et
nous déposais dans un champ de légumes.
Maintenant, je devais me rendre chez moi.
C'est alors qu'une cocinelle volante est
venu me prendre sur elle pour m'apporter
à la maison. En arrivant, maman m'a-
vait préparé un grand bol de fruits
frais avec de la crème fouettée
pour collation.

Catherine Blanchard, 9 ans

Que c'est drôle quand je m'imagine en train de me baigner dans
un lac rempli de fruits. Et puis, j'embarquais sur une chenille
géante. Nous flottions tranquillement quand une grosse grenouille
voulait nous manger. Heureusement, un lutin se trouvait près du
lac et avec son filet magique, il nous attrapait et nous déposait
dans un champ de légumes. Maintenant, je devais me rendre chez
moi. C'est alors qu'une coccinelle volante est venue me prendre
sur elle pour m'apporter à la maison. En arrivant, maman m'avait
préparé un grand bol de fruits frais avec de la crème fouettée
pour collation.

Catherine Blanchard, 9 ans, Granby, QC
École Joseph-Poitevin

Isn't it funny when your lying in bed and you see something flying around the clothesline and you have these dreams about what it might be. Than you decide to check and you get seared and you want to turn back but you just keep going because you want to be brave so you grab your baseball bat on your way to the stairs. then you take a deep breath and start to go down the stairs Step by step by step than you open the sliding doors and you see last weeks dirty underwear on the close line...!!!

By Rob Boone Age 11

Isn't it funny when you're lying in bed and you see something flying around the clothesline and you have these dreams about what it might be. Then you decide to check and you get scared and you want to turn back but you keep going because you want to be brave, so you grab your baseball bat on the way to the stairs. Then you take a deep breath and start to go down the stairs. Step by step by step, then you open the sliding door and you see last week's dirty underwear on the clothesline!

Rob Boone, Age 11, Moncton, NB
Hillcrest School

Que. C'est drôle quand mon
ami Alex vient me visiter.
J'aime entendre son rire
bizarre, c'est contagieux. Il
m'invite à passer des heures
et des heures dans notre
laboratoire : « colex-corporation ».
Il y a une chaise à voyager,
divers robots. Pour son anniversaire, j'ai dormi chez lui. Nous
avons fait des folies. J'ai tellement ri que j'ai eu de la difficulté
à m'endormir. La nuit j'ai
fait des rêves. Alex est allé réveiller Mark. L'usine d'en face faisait des bruits étranges. Au retour, Alex a réalisé que c'était
mon nez qui faisait ce vacarme.
Que c'est drôle dormir chez Alex. Cool !

COLIN Bordeleau 8 1/2 Ans

Que c'est drôle quand mon ami Alex vient me
visiter. J'aime entendre son rire bizarre. C'est
contagieux. Il m'invite à passer des heures et
des heures dans notre laboratoire « colex-
corporation ». Il y a une chaise à voyager,
divers robots. Pour son anniversaire, j'ai dormi chez lui. Nous
avons fait des folies. J'ai tellement ri que j'ai eu de la difficulté
à m'endormir. La nuit, j'ai fait des rêves. Alex est allé réveiller
Mark. L'usine d'en face faisait des bruits étranges. Au retour,
Alex a réalisé que c'était mon nez qui faisait ce vacarme.
Que c'est drôle dormir chez Alex. Cool !

Colin Bordeleau, 8 ans, Shawinigan, QC
École Antoine Hallé

Que c'est drôle quand ma voisine a placé deux ailes multicolores sur sa chatte qui s'est envolée ! Celle-ci s'appelle Biscuit. Sa fourrure est grise et contient des lignes noires. Elle a un nez très mignon et trois longues moustaches de chaque côté. Quand Biscuit s'est envolée, elle a aperçu au loin un avion. Elle s'est rapprochée de celui-ci. Toutes les personnes qui étaient dans l'aéroplane, ont vu la petite chatte. Ensuite, le pilote a perdu contrôle. Alors, c'est ainsi que Biscuit a ouvert la porte de l'avion, a pris la place du conducteur et a fait descendre celle-ci en sécurité.

Nadine Bou Khzam   9 ans

Que c'est drôle quand ma voisine a placé deux ailes multicolores sur sa chatte qui s'est envolée ! Celle-ci s'appelle Biscuit. Sa fourrure est grise et contient des lignes noires. Elle a un nez très mignon et trois longues moustaches de chaque côté. Quand Biscuit s'est envolée, elle a aperçu au loin un avion. Elle s'est rapprochée de celui-ci. Toutes les personnes qui étaient dans l'aéroplane ont vu la petite chatte. Ensuite, le pilote a perdu contrôle. Alors, c'est ainsi que Biscuit a ouvert la porte de l'avion, a pris la place du conducteur et a fait descendre celui-ci en sécurité.

Nadine Bou Khzam, 9 ans, Brossard, QC
École Saint-Laurent

Isn't it funny when your best friend is a big, pink rat? He has a huge eight foot tail! He can run as fast as the speed of light. He is a big rat. He is as big as a giraffe. I like the big rat a lot. The rat likes to eat meat, cheese, bugs, soup, pizza. The rat likes to play poker with his friend Colton. They play together all the day. When he's mad he turns purple. We'll be best friends forever.

Colton Bowyer, Age 8

Isn't it funny when your best friend is a big pink rat? He has a huge eight-foot tail! He can run as fast as the speed of light. He is a big rat. He is as big as a giraffe. I like the big rat a lot. The rat likes to eat meat, cheese, bugs, soup, and pizza. The rat likes to play poker with his friend Colton. They play together all day. When he's mad, he turns purple. We'll be best friends forever.

Colton Bowyer, Age 8, Tompkins, SK
Tompkins School

Que c'est drôle quand la lune fait une grimace au soleil et que le soleil lui en fait une aussi ! C'est que la lune aimerait voir le jour... et le soleil voudrait voir la nuit. La lune est chanceuse, elle a les étoiles comme amies. Le soleil a les nuages et les gouttes de pluie. La lune voit les enfants qui dorment dans leur lit. Le soleil, lui, les voit jouer toute la journée. Ce serait bizarre de voir à midi la lune qui nous sourit... Ou à minuit, le soleil qui rit !

Que c'est drôle quand la lune fait une grimace au soleil et que le soleil lui en fait une aussi ! C'est que la lune aimerait voir le jour… et le soleil voudrait voir la nuit. La lune est chanceuse, elle a les étoiles comme amies. Le soleil a les nuages et les gouttes de pluie. La lune voit les enfants qui dorment dans leur lit. Le soleil, lui, les voit jouer toute la journée. Ce serait bizarre de voir à midi la lune qui nous sourit… Ou à minuit, le soleil qui rit !

**Anne-Rosalie Brassard, 8 ans, Jonquière, QC
École Ste-Cécile**

Que c'est drôle quand je me lève le matin ! J'ai tous les cheveux
en broussaille. On dirait que de minuscules extraterrestres se sont
battus sur le dessus de ma tête. Ces petits inconnus sont venus
visiter notre planète, mais ils ont atterri dans mes cheveux.
Le commandant grimpe sur un cheveu pour voir ce qu'il y a
à l'horizon. Nous sommes perdus, dit-il. Ce que je vois, reprend
le commandant, c'est deux crevasses, (les yeux), une énorme
roche, (le nez), et un gros trou, (la bouche). Ils rentrent alors
dans leur vaisseau et s'en vont en quête d'une nouvelle planète.

Yan Érik Breault Bouchard, 11 ans,
Saint-Henri, QC, École Belleau-Gagnon

Isn't it funny when Bridgett knew this day would come now that it was here, she didn't know if she would laugh or cry. "I won't know anyone," she said again. "Most people don't know anyone at a new school," said Mama. "I won't understand what they say," said Bridgett. "You will look and listen and learn," said Mama. "They won't understand me," said Bridgett. "Any body can talk," said Mama. "Eyes speak many words, and a smile is a smile in language." "Everything here is so different," said Bridgett. "Only on outside," said Mama, "Inside people are the same."

Bridgette, Age 11

Isn't it funny when Bridgette knew this day would come, now that it was here; she didn't know if she would laugh or cry. "I won't know anyone", she said again. "Most people don't know anyone at a new school", said mama. "I won't understand what they say", said Bridgette. "You will look and listen and learn", said mama. "They won't understand me", said Bridgette. "Anybody can talk", said mama. "Eyes speak many words, and a smile is a smile in any language." "Everything here is so different", said Bridgette. "Only on the outside", said mama, "Inside, people are the same."

Bridgette, Age 11, Toronto, ON
Regent Park Duke of York

Que c'est drôle quand on part en voyage dans sa tête et dans son monde imaginaire. J'y vois que de belles choses qui me font rire aux éclats. Un zoo plein d'animaux bizarres avec des pattes longues, longues et nombreuses. Des oreilles grandes qui traînent par terre. On continue le voyage car nous sommes impatients de voir de beaux paysages que nous offre dame nature. Voir la mer pour la première fois et les pieds à l'eau on sent les poissons gruger les orteilles. J'aime voyager dans l'imaginaire.

Émilie Brochu 13 ans

Que c'est drôle quand on part en voyage dans sa tête et dans son monde imaginaire. J'y vois que de belles choses qui me font rire aux éclats. Un zoo plein d'animaux bizarres avec des pattes longues, longues et nombreuses. Des oreilles grandes qui traînent par terre. On continue le voyage, car nous sommes impatients de voir de beaux paysages que nous offre dame nature, voir la mer pour la première fois et les pieds à l'eau, on sent les poissons gruger les orteilles. J'aime voyager dans l'imaginaire.

Emilie Brochu, 13 ans, St-Magloire, QC
Polyvalente des Appalaches

Isn't it funny when you teacher acts strange? I think that they're spys working for the C.I.A. The schoolboard is the association's headquarters where they meet to find out all the information about our families! Their chalk is the mind-readers that read our minds when we're daydreaming in school. Their staplers are tracking devices, so they track us wherever we go. Their desks turn into little offices where they have a file for every kid they ever "taught!" There are so many more devices that I can't remember them all. I'm the only one who knows about it!

Alissa Brothers age:11

Isn't it funny when your teacher acts strange? I think that they are spies working for the C.I.A. The school board is the association's headquarters, where they meet to find out all the information about our families! Their chalk is the mind readers that read our minds when we're daydreaming in school. Their staplers are tracking devices. So wherever we go their desks turn into little offices where they have a file for every kid they ever 'taught'. There are so many more devices, that I could never tell them all. I'm the only one that knows about it!

Alissa Brothers, Age 11, Goulds, NL
Goulds Elementary School

Que c'est drôle quand je voyage avec Julie Payette. C'est difficile d'avoir une conversation sérieuse, car Julie utilise six langues dans une même phrase. Lors du décollage, de gigantesques nuages de mousse nous envahissent. Quelqu'un a rempli les réservoirs avec du savon à vaisselle. En utilisant les réacteurs d'appoint, nous nous éloignons de la Terre et réalisons que celle-ci est complètement recouverte de mousse. Julie et moi sommes estomaquées. Nous allons laisser notre grande trace de mousse dans l'espace. Toutefois, ce canular a permis de nettoyer la planète et laisser une fraîche odeur de citron.

Andréanne Brousseau , 12 ans

Que c'est drôle quand je voyage avec Julie Payette. C'est difficile d'avoir une conversation sérieuse, car Julie utilise six langues différentes dans une même phrase. Lors du décollage, de gigantesques nuages de mousse nous envahissent. Quelqu'un a rempli les réservoirs avec du savon à vaisselle. En utilisant les réacteurs d'appoint, nous nous éloignons de la Terre et réalisons que celle-ci est complètement recouverte de mousse. Julie et moi sommes estomaquées. Nous allons laisser notre grande trace de mousse dans l'espace. Toutefois, ce canular a permis de nettoyer la planète et laisser une fraîche odeur de citron.

Andréanne Brousseau, 12 ans, Gatineau, QC
Collège Saint-Joseph

Isn't it funny when you wake up after a dream, thinking it really happened. I dreamt I was walking down a path and when I walked through some mist, I went back in time. I was at an old school. The teacher was ringing the bell. I ran into the school and sat down. When lunchtime came, a girl named Rebecca shared her molasses sandwich with me. We went outside to play. Then the bell was ringing again and I woke up to hear my alarm. I wanted a molasses sandwich. Isn't it funny...
I don't even like molasses!

Caleigh Burhoe, Age 10, Belle River, PEI
Belfast Consolidated School

Isn't it funny when adults act like kids and kids act like adults. Little girls put lipstick on and dress up like adults with highheel shoes. Little girls like to act like adults and pretend they are shopping. Adults have tantrums in public places just like kids. It's funny to see both kids and adults whining in public. Adults act really funny when they are playing with their kids in a park. They don't realize that other people are watching. Isn't it funny that adults and kids are so much alike!

Stephanie Burrows 9½

Isn't it funny when adults act like kids and kids act like adults. Little girls put lipstick on and dress up like adults with high heel shoes. Little girls like to act like adults and pretend they are shopping. Adults have tantrums in public places just like kids. It's funny to see both kids and adults whining in public. Adults act really funny when they are playing with their kids in a park. They don't realize that other people are watching. Isn't it funny that adults and kids are so much alike!

Stephanie Burrows, Age 9, Mississauga, ON
Lorne Park Public School

Isn't it funny when the monster under your bed isn't really a monster? Isaac learned that the monster under his bed was not what it seemed. Not at all! Isaac had to defeat this creepy monster for good. First he reached for the monster's arm. Oh, his baseball bat! Next Isaac grabbed the monsters messy hair. Hey, his favourite Spiderman underwear! Its big head was a deflated football, a fork and some marbles! Its other arm was daddy's lost putter! Isaac's monster wasn't so scary any more. But the mess Isaac now had to clean up was very very scary.

Madelin Burt-D'Agnillo, age 7

Isn't it funny when the monster under your bed isn't really a monster? Isaac learned that the monster under his bed was not what it seemed. Not at all! Isaac had to defeat this creepy monster for good. First, he reached for the monster's arm. Oh, his baseball bat! Next Isaac grabbed the monster's messy hair. Hey, his favourite Spiderman underwear! Its big head was a deflated football, a fork and some marbles! Its other arm was daddy's lost putter! Isaac's monster wasn't so scary any more. But the mess Isaac now had to clean up was very, very scary.

Madelin Burt-D'Agnillo, Age 7, Maple, ON
Discovery Public School

Isn't it funny when people suit their names. My friend Savannah lived on an African savannah with her Uncle. Grant will grant you any favour. Miya is my'a best friend. I'll bet Cher always shares, and Whoopi has a whoopi cushion. When my friend Fran and Frances get together, Fran says hi, Frances says hi and I just get confused. Our friend Justin is always just in time for school. I think Hank should say Hank you to be polite. And me – my name is Regan – pronounced ray gun, but I don't like space movies at all. Funny, isn't it.

Regan Calicetto, Age 9, Mission, BC
Sandy Hill School

Isn't it funny when you're eating supper and then you're broccoli and brussel sprouts come alive. Well, it happened to me!
One day we were having supper, every one was done except me. Then my broccoli and brussel sprouts came alive. I hit them with my fork and that didn't help. I poured milk on them and they just grew bigger. I ran outside and Scruffy my dog attacked them. They picked up Scruffy and put him in his dog house. So I figured out that the only way to destroy them was to eat them. So I did. YUCH!

Natasha Cameron age 10

Isn't it funny when you're eating super and then your broccoli and brussels sprouts come alive; well it happened to me! One day, we were having supper, everyone was done except me. Then my broccoli and brussels sprouts came alive. I hit them with my fork and that didn't help. I poured milk on them, and they just grew bigger. I ran outside and Scruffy, my dog, attacked them. They picked up Scruffy and put him in his doghouse. So I figured out that the only way to destroy them was to eat them. So I did. YUCK!

Natasha Cameron, Age 10, Port Bevis, NS
Baddeck Academy

Isn't it funny when every night my toys come alive. They dance all night by the light of my night light. They eat breakfast at two oclock and they eat supper at five o'clock. Their favorite dance is ballet except Musical Horse prefers tap dancing. They each argue over the dance. Then Musical Horse starts crying because he never gets his wish to tap dance. Pinky says, "stop fighting because you are making Musical Horse cry. Tonight we can do tap dancing and the next night we can do ballet." This made Musical Horse stop crying. They started to dance.

Dallas Campbell, 8

Isn't it funny when every night my toys come alive. They dance all night by the light of my night-light. They eat breakfast at two o'clock and they eat supper at five o'clock. Their favorite dance is ballet, except musical horse prefers tap dancing. They each argue over the dance. Then musical horse starts crying because he never gets his wish to tap dance. Pinky says, "Stop fighting because you are making musical horse cry. Tonight we can do tap dancing and the next night we can do ballet." This made musical horse stop crying. They started to dance.

Dallas Campbell, Age 8, South Berwick, NS
Berwick & District School

44

Isn't it funny when we, as Canadians, think everything we do is normal? We don't give our customs a second thought because we think they are natural. The only time we look at ourselves critically, is when we observe other cultures. For instance, when we order a double cheeseburger, large fries and a diet Pepsi. Or when our banks leave the doors to the vault wide open and chain the pens to the counter. Or when a pizza can get to your house faster than an ambulance. These few examples show us that the funniest things are in everyday life.

Morgan Campbell, age 13

Isn't it funny when we, as Canadians, think everything we do is normal? We don't give our customs a second thought because we think they are natural. The only time we look at ourselves critically, is when we observe other cultures. For instance, when we order a double cheeseburger, large fries, and a diet Pepsi. Or when our banks leave the doors to the vault wide open and chain the pens to the counter. Or when a pizza can get to your house faster than an ambulance. These few examples show us that the funniest things are in everyday life.

Morgan Campbell, Age 13, Windsor, ON
Maranatha Christian Academy

Isn't it funny when food tastes better at Grandma's? I mean, normally I hate vegetables but as soon as I walk through Grandma's door, I transform into a girl who likes everything. I even like Brussels sprouts when I'm there! When Grandma serves me Brussels sprouts I smile as I happily accept the green leafy monster and allow it to slide down my throat. My mom thinks that food tastes better at Grandma's because Grandma's a better cook than she is. But I know that's not true. Food tastes better at Grandma's because it's made with a special Grandma love.

Amanda Cannon, Age 9

Isn't it funny when food tastes better at Grandma's? I mean, normally I hate vegetables, but as soon as I walk through Grandma's door, I transform into a girl who likes everything. I even like brussels sprouts when I'm there! When Grandma serves me brussels sprouts, I smile as I happily accept the green leafy monster and allow it to slide down my throat. My mom thinks that food tastes better at Grandma's because Grandma's a better cook than she is. But I know that's not true. Food tastes better at Grandma's because it's made with a special Grandma love.

Amanda Cannon, Age 9, Caledon East, ON
Herb Campbell Public School

Isn't it funny when people think that money can buy everything? After all, no amount of money can buy love and friendship. No amount of money can buy respect. But there is a very simple way to attain these things. In order to be loved, you must love. To have a friend, you must be a friend. And to be respected, you must show respect. It sounds so simple, and yet some people never seem to realize that the most important things in life have no monetary value. Some people never realize that money can't buy everything. Funny, isn't it?

Michelle Cannon, Age 11

Isn't it funny when people think that money can buy everything?
After all, no amount of money can buy love and friendship.
No amount of money can buy respect. But there is a very simple
way to attain these things. In order to be loved, you must love.
To have a friend, you must be a friend. And to be respected,
you must show respect. It sounds so simple, and yet some people
never seem to realize that the most important things in life have
no monetary value. Some people never realize that money can't
buy everything. Funny, isn't it?

Michelle Cannon, Age 11, Caledon East, ON
Herb Campbell Public School

Isn't it funny when your goldfish turn into purplefish? The day after we bought our pet fish I woke up to feed them and was shocked to see my goldfish had turned to purplefish. They were trying to flick their pebbles into their fishnet to score a goal. I took a closer look and saw that they were wearing Toronto Raptors Jerseys! Nobody would believe me if I told them so I kept it my own secret and enjoyed the game.

Mark canto Age: 9

Isn't it funny when your goldfish turns into a purple fish? The day after we bought our pet fish, I woke up to feed them and was shocked to see my goldfish had turned to purple fish. They were trying to flick their pebbles into their fish net with their back fins to score a goal. I took a closer look and saw they were wearing Toronto Raptor jerseys! Nobody would believe me if I told them, so I kept it my secret and enjoyed the game.

Mark Canto, Age 9, Markham, ON
St. Vincent de Paul Roman Catholic School

Que c'est drôle quand mon père éternue. C'est très avantageux
parfois. L'automne, on n'a même pas besoin de racler les feuilles.
Mon père réussit à tout balayer en un seul petit éternuement.
Toutes les feuilles se ramassent au village d'à côté. Même mon
oncle François reconnaît nos feuilles sur son terrain ! Mais
l'hiver, ce n'est pas très avantageux. Mon père ne fait seulement
qu'ouvrir la bouche et la maison vient de lever de trois pieds
de terre et le froid glacial vient d'entrer. Heureusement qu'il n'a
pas eu la pneumonie ou pire : le rhume des foins !!! Sacré papa !

Catherine Carbonneau, 11 ans,
Sainte-Hénédine, QC, École La Découverte

Isn't it funny when...One morning I woke up and my clothes were too long! When I brushed my teeth, toothpaste came squirting at my body!. After when I walked to school everybody laughed at me because I looked so messy and I forgot my pants!. When I reached school my friends were laughing at me because they thought I looked so weird and awful! At recesstime I could'nt go out because I remembered I forgot my pants!. My day was so bad at school I just had to laugh.

Alexandria Leilani Cartagena, 9

Isn't it funny when, one morning, I woke up and my clothes were too long! When I brushed my teeth, toothpaste came squirting at my body! After, when I walked to school, everybody laughed at me because I looked so messy and I forgot my pants! When I reached school, my friends were laughing at me because they thought I looked so weird and awful! At recess time, I couldn't go out because I remembered I forgot my pants! My day was so bad at school, I just had to laugh.

Alexandria Leilani Cartagena, Age 9, Vancouver, BC, Corpus Christi School

Isn't it funny when you find a monster swimming in your soup! I called my mom but she didn't believe me, so I went to get my friend. I ran to the arcade as fast as I could. My friend was playing a video game and I asked him if he believed in monsters. He said "Yeah! I believe in them! I'm surrounded by monsters!" I went back home to see if the monster destroyed my house. My mom checked and said "There was no monster in your soup. Those were noodles, you were tricked by a bunch of noodles!"

Julian cassano age 7

Isn't it funny when you find a monster swimming in your soup.
I called my Mom but she didn't believe me, so I went to get
my friend. I ran to the arcade as fast as I could. My friend
was playing a video game, and I asked him if he believed in
monsters. He said, "Yeah! I believe in them! I'm surrounded
my monsters!" I went back home to see if the monster destroyed
my house. My Mom checked and said, "There was no monster
in your soup. Those were noodles, you were tricked by
a bunch of noodles!"

Julian Cassano, Age 7, Mississauga, ON
St. Dunstan School

Isn't it funny when a new family moved into my neighbourhood. All my neighbours acted strange because this family in particular didn't used a trailer they used a Spaceship. They had a girl and she became my friend, She transformed all the bullies in town into clowns. She cleaned my whole room in one Second!, She made ice cream out of mud and marshmellows out of a rock. She transformed the playground into a themepark. In her house the kitchen cook by itself and her dog can fly. She is my best friend every thing is more funny with her around.

francis Castillo, 9 years

Isn't it funny when a new family moved into my neighbourhood. All my neighbours acted strange because this family in particular didn't use a trailer, they used a spaceship. They had a girl and she became my friend; she transformed all the bullies in town into clowns. She cleaned my whole room in one second! She made ice cream out of mud and marshmallows out of a rock. She transformed the playground into a theme park. In her house, the kitchen cooks by itself and her dog can fly. She is my best friend; everything is more funny with her around.

Francis Castillo, Age 9, Calgary, AB
Langenvin School

Que c'est drôle quand un hibou chante des chansons d'amour au lieu de faire des cris épeurants. C'est vraiment drôle quand un vampire, à la place de sucer le sang des gens et des animaux, suce une sucette glacée. C'est encor plus drôle quand une méchante sorcière attrape la grippe car son nez, tellement il est long et croche, coule dans sa bouche. Mais c'est hiper drôle quand un fantôme s'accroche sur un clou et perd sa robe blanche. Tous ces personnages ne font plus peur du tout. Au contraire, ils font rire tous les habitants du village! Joyeuse Halloween!

Marie-Ève Chagnon 9 ans

Que c'est drôle quand un hibou chante des chansons d'amour au lieu de faire des cris épeurants. C'est vraiment drôle quand un vampire, à la place du sucer le sang des gens et des animaux, suce une sucette glacée. C'est encore plus drôle quand une méchante sorcière attrape la grippe car son nez, tellement il est long et croche, coule dans sa bouche. Mais c'est hyper drôle quand un fantôme s'accroche sur un clou et perd sa robe blanche. Tous ces personnages ne font plus peur du tout. Au contraire, ils font rire tous les habitants du village ! Joyeuse Halloween !

Marie-Ève Chagnon, 9 ans, St-Hubert, QC
École des Milles-Fleurs

Isn't it funny when, walking to school, I was blowing a gigantic bubble and next thing I knew, I was floating up into space! I landed on Mars and made a friend named Xybavmc. It was pretty safe, except for meteorites AHHHH! WATCH OUT, one was coming right at me! Thank goodness my bubble protected me. I found Xybavmc right away and I asked him, "Do you have a cannon; I want to go home?" I put on a crash helmet and was blasted home. Then I said, "I WILL NEVER BLOW A BUBBLE AGAIN!"

Kevin Chambers, Age 9, Edmonton, AB
Crawford Plains School

Que c'est drôle quand ma perruche panique et fonce dans tour les murs. Ma perruche à la tête rouge, avec les ailes violettes et un oeil jaune et l'autre bleu. Elle est très bizarre parce qu'elle a une patte de bois, elle est fluoréscente dans le noir et elle chante très, très faux. Elle sait parler mais elle dit m'importe quoi. Moi je l'adore mais ma mère a peur d'elle parce que quand elle lui donne à manger elle la mord. Elle mange seulement des Smarties rouge. Au fait, son nom c'est Pout-Pout et aussi elle aime tout le monde.

Raphaïlle Chénard Gagnon, Âge 10

Que c'est drôle quand ma perruche panique et fonce dans tous les murs. Ma perruche à la tête rouge, avec les ailes violettes et un ocil jaune et l'autre bleu. Elle est très bizarre, parce qu'elle a une patte de bois, elle est fluorescente dans le noir et elle chante très, très faux. Elle sait parler, mais elle dit n'importe quoi. Moi je l'adore, mais ma mère a peur d'elle, parce que quand elle lui donne à manger, elle la mord. Elle mange seulement des Smarties rouges. Au fait, son nom c'est Pout-Pout et aussi elle aime tout le monde.

**Raphaïlle Chénard Gagnon, 10 ans,
Rimouski, QC, École Sainte-Agnès**

Isn't it funny when you get ants in your pants? You run to your room and you throw your pants in the dirty clothes. You get new pants on. Your mom picks up the pants and the ants go up your hands. She runs to the sink. She washes her hands where dad shaves his face. Later, they go up Dad's face. He runs to the dog dish. The dog drinks and the ants go up his nose. He runs to the door, and the ants go outside the door and in the hole.

Kevin Chevalier, Age 10, Leamington, ON
Mt. Carmel-Blytheswood

Isn't it funny when you read a great comic? I'm going to tell you about my friend Clarissa. She definitely learned it's not good to have too much of one thing! Last year Clarissa always read Superdog Comics. One day when she was reading she got sucked into the comic! "Ahhhhh", Clarissa screamed. She opened her eyes and saw Superdog. "WOW!", exclaimed Clarissa. "Hello!", said Superdog. "Can you help me?" "How?", asked Clarissa. "I need you to.........Bbbrrriinngg." Clarissa opened her eyes and was in her room! Clarissa never read Superdog comics again. Well, maybe just once in a while!

Kendra Chisholm, 11

Isn't it funny when you read a great comic? I'm going to tell you about my friend Clarissa. She definitely learned it's not good to have too much of one thing! Last year, Clarissa always read Superdog comics. One day, when she was reading, she got sucked into the comic! "Ahhhhh", Clarissa screamed. She opened her eyes and saw Superdog! "WOW", exclaimed Clarissa. "Hello", said Superdog, "Can you help me?" "How?", asked Clarissa. "I need you to....bbbbbrrriiinnngg." Clarissa opened her eyes and was in her room. Clarissa never read Superdog comics again. Well, maybe just once in a while!

Kendra Chisholm, Age 11, Lower Sackville, NS, Gertrude Parker Elementary

Isn't it funny when you see a rocket launch, you start wondering. Wondering what the astronauts will do, what they'll see. You tell yourself, if I were an astronaut I'd jump on the moon. I'd see if it's really made of cheese. I'd meet aliens and invite them to Earth. You realize how spectacular astronauts are and you want to be spectacular too. You decide to become one. You realize it's harder than jumping on the moon. The day comes when you're ready too go to space, you put on your spacesuit and say, "Without wondering, I wouldn't be here".

Anna Chouchkova age.11

Isn't it funny when you see a rocket launch, you start wondering. Wondering what the astronauts will do, what they'll see. You tell yourself, if I was an astronaut I'd jump on the moon. I'd see if it's made of cheese. I'd meet aliens and invite them to Earth. You realize how spectacular astronauts are and you want to be spectacular too. You decide to become one. You realize it's harder than jumping on the moon. When the day comes, when you're ready to go to space, you put on your space suit and say, "Without wondering, I wouldn't be here!"

Anna Chouchkova, Age 11, Toronto, ON
Brown Public School

"Isn't it funny when you see those clowns with those frowns?" Rhymer would say. Well, that's not his real name! Let me tell you the story of Fred...

Born with funny parents and friends, Fred was always funny. He made everyone smile, then people got bored after a while.

He went to the mountains to get good advice. There, he met some wise talking mice. They tell him, "Think of a twist!" "What about rhyming?" said Fred, clenching his fist!

Pass on the story of Rhymer, now an old man, but remember to start it with "Isn't it funny when..."

Lorraine Chuen, 12

"Isn't it funny when you see those clowns with those frowns?" Rhymer would say. Well, that's not his real name. Let me tell you the story of Fred. Born with funny parents and friends, Fred was always funny. He made everyone smile, then people got bored after a while. He went to the mountains to get good advice. There, he met some wise-talking mice. They tell him, "Think of a twist." "What about rhyming," said Fred, clenching his fist! Pass on the story of Rhymer, now an old man, but remember to start it with "Isn't it funny when..."

Lorraine Chuen, Age 12, Trenton, ON
St. Mary's School

"Isn't it funny, when" a song gets stuck in your head.

One day, I went to school humming the Flintstones song. Soon all my friends were humming it. We were humming it in gym class and then the teacher started humming. After lunch I heard one teacher telling another teacher that she couldn't get that song out of her head. Soon the other teacher started humming it too. This was so funny because I didn't have the song in my head anymore but everyone else did. On my way home, I heard someone singing it. Oh no, not again!!

Christine Clogg - Age 10

Isn't it funny when a song gets stuck in your head. One day, I went to school humming the Flintstones song. Soon, all my friends were humming it. We were humming it in gym class, and then the teacher started humming. After lunch, I heard one teacher telling another teacher that she couldn't get that song out of her head. Soon, the other teacher started humming it too. This was so funny because I didn't have the song in my head anymore, but everyone else did. On my way home, I heard someone singing it. Oh no, not again!

Christine Clogg, Age 10, Kirkland, QC
Allancroft School

Isn't it funny when clouds appear to be different shapes and objects? As I lay on the grass, my eyes took in the domed heavens with peaceful bliss. Suddenly, an odd creature immerged from the tranquil white clouds. As soon as I could decipher it, I realized it was an animal made almost completely out of water! It was floating daintily with the wind, blending in perfectly with sky. Abruptly the silence broke...
"Jason, get your head out of the clouds and listen!" Isn't it funny when you are sent to the principal's office for discovering a new species?

Alexandra Coates, age 13

Isn't it funny when clouds appear to be different shapes and objects? As I lay on the grass, my eyes took in the domed heavens with peaceful bliss. Suddenly, an odd creature emerged from the tranquil white clouds. As soon as I could decipher it, I realized it was an animal made almost completely out of water! It was floating daintily with the wind, blending in perfectly with the sky. Abruptly the silence broke... "Jason, get your head out of the clouds and listen!" Isn't it funny when you are sent to the principal's office for discovering a new species?

**Alexandra Coates, Age 13, Calgary, AB
École Elboya Elementary Junior High**

61

Que c'est drôle quand je vois tes plumes brillantes voler dans le vent et que les rayons du soleil reflètent sur tes plumes. Quand je t'ai vu sortir de ta coquille, j'ai tout de suite commencé à rire. Que c'est drôle quand tu manges tes graines. Je suis heureux. J'aime te regarder quand tu es sur ton perchoir. Quand tu es parti de ton perchoir et que tu t'es envolé dans la maison, je me suis tout de suite dit que maman devait t'acheter une cage.

FIN

Alexis Curodeau-Codère 8 ans

Que c'est drôle quand je vois tes plumes brillantes voler dans le vent et que les rayons du soleil reflètent sur tes plumes. Quand je t'ai vu sortir de ta coquille, j'ai tout de suite commencé à rire. Que c'est drôle quand tu manges tes graines. Je suis heureux. J'aime te regarder quand tu es sur ton perchoir. Quand tu es parti de ton perchoir et que tu t'es envolé dans la maison, je me suis tout de suite dit que maman devait t'acheter une cage. FIN.

Alexis Curodeau-Codère, 8 ans, Verdun, QC
École Notre-Dame-de-la-Garde

Isn't it funny when you show up at class late so your teacher gives you a detention. Everyone thinks you'll come out a new person. In Detention Room Number two, you come out a whole new species! When Tommy Griffin had detention, he simply walked in. His detention was for twenty minutes. When his time was up, everyone heard dog barking. A slightly large dog came walking by everyone with Tommy's shoes and backpack on him. Don't you understand!? Tommy is now a dog!!! No one knows what goes on in detention, but if you understood dog, Tommy'd tell you!

Olivia D'Alessandro 10

Isn't it funny when you show up at class late, so your teacher gives you a detention. Everyone thinks you'll come out a new person, but in detention room number two, you come out a whole new species! When Tommy Griffin had detention, he simply walked in. His detention was for twenty-five minutes. When his time was up, everyone heard dog barking. A slightly large dog came walking by everyone, with Tommy's shoes and backpack on him. Don't you understand? Tommy is now a dog! No one knows what goes on in detention, but if you understood dog, Tommy'd tell you!

Olivia D'Alessandro, Age 10, Mississauga, ON
St. Thomas More

Que c'est drôle quand Elizabeth vient me visiter. Elle est mon joujou préféré. Pendant qu'elle dort, je lui chatouille les hanches, car c'est son point sensible. Quand je me cache sur le bateau, je lui fais piquer des sauts et elle tombe à l'eau comme une truite. Mais elle est futée Elizabeth, elle nage sous l'eau et revient m'attraper par les pieds. Elle me fait boire un bon bouillon d'eau du lac. J'aime Elizabeth, parce que c'est mon jouet favori sur terre et sur mer. Elizabeth, c'est ma « grosse grenouille verte ».

Catherine Dallaire-Lagacé, 9 ans,
Charlesbourg, QC, École Cap-Soleil

Isn't it funny when a beautiful dream turns into a laugh? You appear in a magical, tropical rainforest. You see a bright rainbow of many colours. Infront of this rainbow is a princess. She is graceful with long, golden hair. She seems to know your name as she calls you over. She places a pink rose in your hair as she asks you if you have seen her pet toad, Wart. You laugh and help her look. In what feels like no time, you find Wart hidden in a tiny glass slipper. She thanks you as you drift back to sleep.

Angela DeGagne ★Age-13

Isn't it funny when a beautiful dream turns into a laugh?
You appear in a magical, tropical rainforest. You see a bright
rainbow of many colours. In front of this rainbow is a princess.
She is graceful with long, golden hair. She seems to know your
name as she calls you over. She places a pink rose in your hair
as she asks if you have seen her pet toad, Wart. You laugh and
help her look. In what feels like no time, you find Wart hidden
in a tiny glass slipper. She thanks you as you drift back to sleep.

Angela DeGagne, Age 13, Selkirk, MB
Happy Thought School

Isn't it funny when something unexpected happens to you? It comes flying out of the sky and it hits you! Peggy Sues day started off great. Nothing could of been better. Her hair was great, her clothes matched, and she managed to get the last waffle from the freezer. The morning was great until lunch, when a hard candy hits the side of her head. She had two choices. She could have been embarrassed or she could have opened the wrapper popped the candy in her mouth, and carried on with her awesome day! She chose the awesome day!

Kaitlyn DeGasperis Age 11

Isn't it funny when something unexpected happens to you?
It comes flying out of the sky and it hits you! Peggy Sue's day
started off great. Nothing could have been better. Her hair was
great, her clothes matched and she managed to get the last waffle
from the freezer. The morning was great until lunch, when a hard
candy hit the side of her head. She had two choices. She could
have been embarrassed or she could have opened the wrapper,
popped the candy in her mouth, and carried on with her
awesome day! She chose the awesome day!

Kaitlyn DeGasperis, Age 11, St. Catharines, ON
St. Peter's School

Isn't it funny when a camel eats spaghetti? A camel eats spaghetti with a whole bunch in his mouth! But not off a plate, off the ground! He doesn't use a fork, he just slurps it up with his mouth! He doesn't eat the sauce with the spaghetti, he drinks it after out of a cup. I know because I have a camel named Herman. He has ten humps because he is ten years old. Herman knows a monkey named Pete. Pete likes to eat pizza. Some days Herman and Pete eat pizza together because they are best friends.

Jennifer Delainey, 7

Isn't it funny when a camel eats spaghetti? A camel eats spaghetti with a whole bunch in his mouth! But not off a plate, off the ground! He doesn't use a fork; he just slurps it up with his mouth! He doesn't eat the sauce with the spaghetti; he drinks it after out of a cup. I know because I have a camel named Herman. He has ten humps because he is ten years old. Herman knows a monkey named Pete. Pete likes to eat pizza. Some days, Herman and Pete eat pizza together because they are best friends.

**Jennifer Delainey, Age 7, St. Albert, AB
Leo Nickerson School**

Isn't it funny when the domino effect results from
another's mistake and so on? For example, once when
Jim came home from school, he put down his hat (which
he won free at a baseball game) on the kitchen table. Then
the doorbell rang. His sister answered the door to one of
Jim's friends who forgot his identical free hat at Jim's house.
She gave him Jim's hat thinking it was the right one.
Jim's hat kept going from person to person because
each individual thought it was their free hat
that was missing. Can't life be odd?

Adam Dermer   11 yrs. old

Isn't it funny when the domino effect results from another's mistake and so on? For example, once when Jim came home from school, he put down his hat (which he was given free at a baseball game) on the kitchen table. Then the doorbell rang. His sister answered the door to one of Jim's friends who forgot his identical free hat at Jim's house. She gave him Jim's hat, thinking it was the right one. Jim's hat kept going from person to person because each individual thought it was their free hat that was missing. Can't life be odd?

Adam Dermer, Age 11, Westmount, QC
St-Georges School of Montreal

Que c'est drôle quand un mammouth se baigne dans ma piscine avec mon amie la licorne. Ma taupe avait très peur de cela, car ce n'est pas tous les jours qu'un mammouth et une licorne se baignent dans une piscine. Les éléphants les trouvaient spéciaux car le mammouth était plutôt énorme et la licorne se trouvait unique. Elle était heureuse. En sortant, le mammouth avait transporté avec lui toute l'eau de la piscine. Alors, la piscine était vide ! J'ai donc été obligé de la remplir. Le mammouth et la licorne partent patte dans la patte dans leur monde rigolo.

David Desjardins, 11 ans, Montréal, QC
École Notre-Dame

Que c'est drôle quand les gens accourent pour me décrocher. Aussi bien vous le dire tout de suite, je ne suis qu'un téléphone. Mais être ce que je suis a de nombreux avantages. Je peux discrètement écouter toutes les conversations qui sont souvent très intrigantes. Quand je m'ennuie, je peux jouer avec mon très proche voisin le répondeur et mon ami l'annuaire. Mais mon copain l'annuaire nous quitte à chaque année et revient de plus en plus beau avec plus de numéros. Parfois, les gens me prennent sans arrêt et cela m'énerve. Mais ma revanche, c'est la facture du téléphone...

Marie-Ève Deslauriers, 11 ans

Que c'est drôle quand les gens accourent pour me décrocher. Aussi bien vous le dire tout de suite, je ne suis qu'un téléphone. Mais être ce que je suis a de nombreux avantages. Je peux discrètement écouter toutes les conversations qui sont souvent très intrigantes. Quand je m'ennuie, je peux jouer avec mon très proche voisin, le répondeur et mon ami, l'annuaire. Mais mon copain l'annuaire nous quitte à chaque année et revient de plus en plus beau avec plus de numéros. Parfois, les gens me prennent sans arrêt et cela m'énerve. Mais ma revanche, c'est la facture du téléphone…

Marie-Ève Deslauriers, 11 ans,
Cap-de-la-Madeleine, QC, Monseigneur Comtois

Isn't it funny when you take a ten dollar bill to church and it seems so big but when you take it to the grocery store it is not so big at all. Isn't it funny how long it takes you to do your chores but playing sixty minutes of basketball is nothing. Isn't it funny when carrots are supposed to be so good for your eyes but yet we see so many dead rabbits on the road. Isn't it funny when people scramble to get a front seat at a game of concert but scramble to get the back seat at church. Andrew Doucette Age 12

Isn't it funny when you take a ten dollar bill to church. It's so big but when you take it to the grocery store, it is not so big at all. Isn't it funny how long it takes you to do your chores, but playing sixty minutes of basketball is nothing. Isn't it funny when carrots are supposed to be so good for your eyes, but yet we see so many dead rabbits on the road. Isn't it funny when people scramble to get a front seat at a game or concert, but scramble to get the back at church.

Andrew Doucette, Age 12, Saint John, NB
Forest Hills School

Isn't it funny when parents say things that confuse kids? Here are a few of my personal favourites: "Will you smart'n up!"... "Don't be so smart". "It's not polite to stare!"... "Look at me when I'm talking to you!" "Keep it up young man!"... "Stop it right now!" "Take your time and do it well!"... "Hurry up and get it done!" "You should be ashamed of yourself!"... "I hope you're proud of yourself!" "Answer me when I'm talking to you!"... "Don't talk back to me!" Parents are funny, aren't they?

Vanessa Eastman, Age 12

Isn't it funny when parents say things that confuse kids? Here are a few of my personal favourites: "Will you smart'n up!"... "Don't be so smart". "It's not polite to stare!"... "Look at me when I'm talking to you!" "Keep it up young man!"... "Stop it right now!" "Take your time and do it well!"... "Hurry up and get it done!" "You should be ashamed of yourself!"... "I hope you're proud of yourself!" "Answer me when I'm talking to you!"... "Don't talk back to me!" Parents are funny, aren't they?

Vanessa Eastman, Age 12, Petrolia, ON
Queen Elizabeth II School

Isn't it funny when you go to an aquarium called, "Angry Fruit"? You start going to a tank, but realize it's not fish swimming, but man-eating bananas. In another tank, there's a giant papaya. In yet another, there's an eight pitted peach! It's kind of boring, but finally something worth watching. A presentation on sharks. The guy who's doing the presentation is saying that sharks had only killed three people last year. He pulled out a bag. He said the deadly thing in the bag had killed more people than sharks. He reached in and pulled out... a coconut?

Courtney Edgar, Age 10

Isn't it funny when you go to an aquarium called 'Angry Fruit'? You start going to a tank, but realize it's not fish swimming, but a man eating bananas. In another tank, there's a giant papaya. In yet another, there's an eight-pitted peach! It's kind of boring, but finally something worth watching. A presentation on sharks. The guy who's doing the presentation is saying that sharks had only killed three people last year. He pulled out a bag. He said the deadly thing in the bag had killed more people than sharks. He reached in and pulled out... a coconut!

Courtney Edgar, Age 10, Calgary, AB
Delta West Academy

Isn't it funny when you jump and your shoes fall off. One day there was a little ant named Arthur. He was so ting his mom could not find shoes to fit his little feet. At school one day he tried skipping with his friends but his shoes kept falling off. So he stuck gum in his shoes to make them stay on. Now he doesn't have trouble keeping his shoes on his feet. But now his shoes don't come off either. The end!!!

Kamea Fenez. Age 8

Isn't it funny when you jump and your shoes fall off. One day, there was a little man named Arthur. He was so tiny, his mom could not find shoes to fit his little feet. At school one day, he tried skipping with his friend but his shoes kept falling off. So he stuck gum in his shoes to make them stay on. Now, he doesn't have trouble keeping his shoes on his feet. But now his shoes don't come off either. The End!!!

Kamea Fenez, Age 8, Saskatoon, SK
Christian Center Academy

Isn't it funny when an elephant tries to blow bubbles with his trunk? I was blowing bubbles one day when an elephant came clumping along and stole my bubbles. He also stole a pipe and a bowl. He poured the bubbles into a bowl and tried to put the pipe into his trunk but it tickled so much that he sneezed. He stuck his trunk into the bubbles and tried to blow a bubble. He started to hiccup like crazy and then "A-choo". He sneezed a tremendous sneeze. So for the rest of his life he never blew bubbles agian.

Brea Fisk   age 11

Isn't it funny when an elephant tries to blow bubbles with his trunk? I was blowing bubbles one day when an elephant came clumping along and stole my bubbles. He also stole a pipe and a bowl. He poured the bubbles into the bowl and tried to blow a bubble. He started to hiccup like crazy and then "A-choo." He sneezed a tremendous sneeze. So for the rest of his life, he never blew bubbles again.

Brea Fisk, Age 11, St. Martin, MB
Peonan Point School

Que c'est drôle quand une cantaloupe s'appelle Grincheuse elle vit avec une banane, Grincheuse s'obstine toujours avec la banane, La cantaloupe c'est meilleur que les bananes, et la banane répond toujours tu es une Grosse cantaloupe pourrie, Tu sais bien que tout le monde adore les bananes. Un jour une pêche arrive avec eux et dit pourquoi est-ce que vous vous disputé pour ça? Vous savez que tout le monde adore les fruits. Depuis ce jour elles sont devenues de très bonnes amies.

Fléchanne Francoeur 7 ans

Que c'est drôle quand un cantaloup s'appelle Grincheuse vit avec une banane. Grincheuse s'obstine toujours avec la banane. Le cantaloup, c'est meilleur que les bananes, et la banane répond toujours tu es un gros cantaloup pourri. Tu sais bien que tout le monde adore les bananes. Un jour, une pêche arrive avec eux et dit: « Pourquoi est-ce que vous vous disputez pour ça ? » Vous savez que tout le monde adore les fruits. Depuis ce jour, elle sont devenues de très bonnes amies.

**Fléchanne Francoeur, 7 ans,
St-Paul de Joliette, QC, Institut Laflèche**

Isn't it funny when you get out of bed, and your hair is dyed red. Then you walk into your bathroom and it look's alot like your classroom. You go down to the table, and beside you sits Mr. Able. You say, "Mr. Able what are you doing at my table?" Then he replied, "I am simply trying to eat some flies." Then you walk to school, and you fall into a pool. After that you're late for class, because you're swimming twenty laps. When you finally get there, in your chair there's a bear, but I don't care!

Katy Fudge   10

Isn't it funny when you get out of bed and your hair is dyed red. Then you walk into your bathroom and it looks a lot like your classroom. You go down to the table and beside you sits Mr. Able. You say, "Mr. Able, what are you doing at my table," then he replied, "I am simply trying to eat some flies." Then you walk to school and you fall into a pool. After that, you're late for class because you're swimming twenty laps. When you finally get there, in your chair there's a bear, but I don't care!

Katy Fudge, Age 10, Bradford, ON
Fieldcrest Elementary School

Que c'est drôle quand madame Bichon sort de la coiffiserie ! Elle y va presque tous les jours. La coiffiserie est un salon de coiffure où on fait des coiffures en forme de bonbons. Les coiffeuse sont des extraterrestres venues sur terre il y a quelques mois. Elles ont tellement aimé les bonbons qu'elles ont décidé de faire un salon de coiffure où les coiffures sont en forme de bonbons. Elles ont mélangé les mots "coiffure" et "confiserie" pour donner le nom "coiffiserie". Madame Bichon s'est fait faire la coiffure : "aux milles bonbons". Elle a l'air bonne ! J'irai peut-être un jour ?

Gabrielle Gagné, 9 ans

Que c'est drôle quand Madame Bichon sort de la coiffiserie ! Elle y va presque tous les jours. La coiffiserie est un salon de coiffure où on fait des coiffures en forme de bonbons. Les coiffeuses sont des extraterrestres venues sur terre il y a quelques mois. Elles ont tellement aimé les bonbons qu'elles ont décidé de faire un salon de coiffure où les coiffures sont en forme de bonbon. Elles ont mélangé les mots « coiffure » et « confiserie », pour donner le nom « coiffiserie ». Madame Bichon s'est fait faire la coiffure « aux mille bonbons ». Elle a l'air bon ! J'irai peut-être un jour !

Gabrielle Gagné, 9 ans, Québec, QC
École La Chaumière

Isn't it funny when the wind blows you to the sky? Well that happened to Timby and it was funny! Timby was walking past the lake and a cool gust of wind blew her right into the cool night sky! She screamed but the wind pushed up in her mouth making her soundproof! She started to happily smile as she saw the moon and stars sparkle and light up the cool night sky. But then a shool of birds flew over her. Four cold white birds pooped right on her head! This is a story she will never forget!

Chloë Gagnon Age: 10

Isn't it funny when the wind blows you to the sky? Well that happened to Timby and it was funny! Timby was walking past the lake and a cool gust of wind blew her right in to the shining night sky! She screamed, but the wind pushed up in her mouth, making her soundproof! She started to happily smile as she saw the moon and stars sparkle and light up the cool night sky. But then, a school of birds flew over her. Four cold, white birds pooped right on her head! This is a story she will never forget!

Chloë Gagnon, Age 10, Sudbury, ON
Adamsdale School

Isn't it funny when you fall asleep in your bed one night and wake up surrounded by sixteen other calculators. You hear the roar of your fellow classmates just coming in for class. I am getting taken down off the shelf and I am picked out by my crush, Beckey. She presses the number four and multiplies it by eight. I give her the answer and she puts me back into the filled bucket of calculators. I weep and moan for somebody to get me out of here. Then finally after three hours, I wake up in my bed.

Tyler Gagnon age : 12

Isn't it funny when you fall asleep in your bed one night and wake up surrounded by sixteen other calculators. You hear the roar of your fellow classmates just coming in for class. I am getting taken down off the shelf and I am picked out from my crush, Beckey. She presses the number four and she multiples it by eight. I give her the answers and she puts me back into the filled bucket of calculators. I weep and moan for somebody to get me out of here. Then finally, after three hours, I wake up in my bed.

Tyler Gagnon, Age 12, Barrie, ON
Andrew Hunter Elementary School

Isn't it funny when you and your dad are in the car and he gets lost? How about lost while listening to oldies? How about lost while listening to your dad singing oldies?

If you are lost with your dad, does he keep pointing out objects along the road and saying, "That's on the way," only to pass it again in ten minutes? This is what journeying with my dad is like.

There is one big plus, though, and that's that I get to spend more time with my dad!

By: Katie Gammie, 13

Isn't it funny when you and your dad are in the car and he gets lost? How about lost while listening to oldies? How about lost while listening to your dad singing oldies? If you are lost with your dad, does he keep pointing out objects along the road and saying "That's on the way," only to pass it again in ten minutes? This is what journeying with my dad is like. There is one big plus, though, and that's that I get to spend more time with my dad!

Katie Gammie, Age 13, Fonthill, ON
St. Alexander School

Isn't it funny when the washer seemed to come alive? Wasn't a lot humorous when you were five? When your shadow ran away at night, and when it came out to play in the light? The boogie man used to live under my bed, wasn't that something to dread? The closet monster hung around, on your door he used to pound. The creaking noises in the house, really it was just a mouse. Cooking for the first time, and when you decided to eat a lime. The milk was spilled on the floor. I begin to remember more and more.

**Claire Gaudreau, Age 12, Ste. Thérèse, PQ,
Rosemère High School**

Que c'est drôle quand je repense au passé. Dans le passé, j'ai
été petite, je ne savais ni parler, ni marcher. Il y a aussi eu mes
arrière-grands-parents, qui vivaient à l'ancienne, à leur manière,
et que j'aurais bien aimé connaître. Avant, bien avant, il y eut
les princesses, les chevaliers, les pyramides, les dinosaures et
avant encore, la formation de la terre. Et avant ? Nous n'étions
qu'une poussière dans l'univers, un espoir, une pensée lointaine.
Et maintenant, tout un monde est créé. Peut-être qu'un jour,
tout basculera ! Oui, c'est vraiment drôle d'y penser,
et bien bizarre aussi.

Marion Gingras-Gagné, 12 ans, Laval, QC
École Georges-Vanier

Que c'est amusant quand je nage dans un océan fait de lait au chocolat. Le sable est fait de bonbons en poudre, les coquillages en gommes ballounes, les arbres en bâtons de canelle et les feuilles en argent. Mon bâteau est fait de bonbons durs et le moteur en chocolat. Les poissons sont faits de 'SKITTLES' et les méduses aussi. J'arrive sur une île avec des noix de cocoa dans lesquelles il y a du cocoa chaud. La nourriture sur cette île est des coquillages en gomme balloune. C'est amusant de nager dans un océan imaginaire.

Haley Goguen, Age 10, Regina, SK
Monseigneur de Laval

Isn't it funny when you see an elephant parading down the street wearing polka-dot underwear! Followed by a zebra with a long neck and blue stripes! OH NO! Here comes a lion. Huhh?! He's got big grey floppy ears?! Phew! Here comes something normal. A mother duck. Wait!, what are those behind her? Hey!, those aren't ducklings, those are waddling frogs with beaks! Then two spotted bears stopped and out of the fancy cage they'd been carrying stepped a rhino with a crown! It bellowed, "Hello, are you awake? Get up!" Everyone awoke, it was all a silly old dream!!

Samantha Goldsmith   9

Isn't it funny when you see an elephant parading down the street wearing polka-dot underwear! Followed by a zebra with a long neck and blue stripes! OH NO! Here comes a lion. Huhh?! He's got big, grey floppy ears?! Phew! Here comes something normal, a mother duck. Wait! What are those behind her? Hey! Those aren't ducklings, those are waddling frogs with beaks. Then, two spotted bears stopped and out of the fancy cage they'd been carrying stepped a rhino with a crown! It bellowed, "Hello, are you awake? Get up!" Everyone awoke; it was all just a silly dream!

Samantha Goldsmith, Age 9, Orillia, ON
Guardian Angels' School

Isn't it funny when you have the hiccups and can't stop. Mrs. McDonald was in a very important meeting at Hobby Farm International giving a presentation on pigs and slop when she began to hiccup. She tried the old tricks of drinking water and holding her breath but the hiccups persisted. Mrs. McDonald went on with a hiccup here and a hiccup there all through her presentation. People were laughing here and people were laughing there. On the way home Mrs. McDonald said to herself, "eee-yi, eee-yi, hiccup O!" Meanwhile the people at the presentation were still laughing here and there.

Jane Grant, 13

Isn't it funny when you have hiccups and can't stop. Mrs. McDonald was in a very important meeting at Hobby Farm International, giving a presentation on pigs and slop, when she began to hiccup. She tried the old tricks of drinking water and holding her breath, but the hiccups persisted. Mrs. McDonald went on with a hiccup here and a hiccup there, all through her presentation. People were laughing here, and people were laughing there. On the way home, Mrs. McDonald said to herself, "Eee-yi, eee-yi, hiccup O!" Meanwhile, the people at the presentation were still laughing here and there.

Jane Grant, Age 13, Edmonton, AB
Kenilworth Junior High

Isn't it funny when brothers are over-protective of their little sisters? I used to think so. Once at the park, while I was skipping along the edge of a wading pool, my brother yelled at me to get off. Ignoring him I jumped into the pool instead. Panicked, my brother ran over to rescue me. When I didn't sink out of sight, he paused, mouth wide open. Was I actually walking on water? Looking down, he saw me standing in just five centimeters of water! Now I realize I am lucky to have a brother who looks out for me.

Nicole Gretes 13

Isn't it funny when brothers are over-protective of their little sisters? I used to think so. Once at the park, while I was skipping along the edge of a wading pool, my brother yelled at me to get off. Ignoring him, I jumped into the pool instead. Panicked, my brother ran over to rescue me. When I didn't sink out of sight, he paused, mouth wide open. Was I actually walking on water? Looking down, he saw me standing in just five centimeters of water! Now I realize I am lucky to have a brother who looks out for me.

Nicole Gretes, Age 13, Toronto, ON
Northern Secondary School

Isn't it funny when you wake up as an animal. I woke up as a tiger!.. I was so scared because I was not myself anymore. I wanted to go outside to run around. There were two guys in a van. They were zoo keepers. They were trying to catch me! They almost caught me but I ran faster than them. Then I went in the circus in the big tent. I went in it and there was a man who was scared. He said "help!" So I ran out of the tent Then I went home.

Nathan Guilatco, 8 yrs old

Isn't it funny when you wake up as an animal. I woke up as a tiger! I was so scared because I was not myself anymore. I wanted to go outside to run around. There were two guys in a van. They were zookeepers. They were trying to catch me! They almost caught me but I ran faster than them. Then, I went in the circus in the big tent. I went in it and there was a man who was scared. He said, "Help!" so I ran out of the tent, then I went home.

Nathan Guilatco, Age 8, Hamilton, ON
St. Helen School

Isn't it funny when a monkey works in a office building. He writes with the wrong side of his pen and puts banana peels on the one hundred dollar carpet. He would replace everything. At the end of the day he went home and had banana soup for dinner. He sleeps in a giant hollowed out banana. In the morning he had a banana bagal for breakfast. He went to work in a banana shaped lemo. When He got to work all the workers hid. He was ready for another day of trouble.

Jessie Gunness age 8

Isn't it funny when a monkey works in an office building. He writes with the wrong side of his pen and leaves banana peels on the one hundred-dollar carpet. He would replace everything. At the end of the day, he went home and he had banana soup for dinner. He slept in a giant hollowed-out banana. In the morning, he had a banana bagel for breakfast. He went to work in a banana-shaped limo. When he got to work, all the workers hid. He was ready for another day of trouble.

Jessie Gunness, Age 8, Muncho Lake, BC
Toad River School

Isn't it funny when you think
so much that your brain explodes?
It happened to me during a huge
spelling test. My head popped open
and tons of words rushed out.
Everybody in the class was reaching
out for the words they needed. The
teacher said "freeze" and everyone
froze, even the words did! "Now
this is how it's going to be," she
said. "The words are going back into
Caleb's head and we will get on
with the test!" The words
listened to the teacher, and so did
all of the kids, even me.

Caleb J. Guy   age: 9

Isn't it funny when you think so much that your brain explodes?
It happened to me during a huge spelling test. My head popped
open and tons of words rushed out. Everybody in the class was
reaching out for the words they needed. The teacher said,
"freeze," and everyone froze, even the words did! Wow, this is
how it's going to be," she said, "The words are going back into
Caleb's head and we will get on with the test." The words
listened to the teacher, and so did all of the kids, even me.

Caleb J. Guy, Age 9, Leduc, AB
Linsford Park School

Que c'est drôle quand Charles le ver de terre essaye de conduire. Charles vit sur une île dans l'océan Atlantique. Il vit dans une pomme. Son copain Justin vit dans une banane tout près de lui. Un jour, Charles alla voir Gertrude la mouche. Gertrude donne des cours de conduite. Charles et Justin jouèrent un tour à Gertrude. Charles avait un moniteur sur lui alors Justin pouvait communiquer avec lui. Tout allait bien jusqu'à ce que Gertrude découvrit le mystère. Soudainement, Charles perdit le contrôle alors il n'a jamais réussit son permis de conduite. À sa centième essai, il abandonna.

Rachel Haché-11 ans

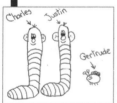

Que c'est drôle quand Charles le ver de terre essaye de conduire. Charles vit sur une île dans l'océan Atlantique. Il vit dans une pomme. Son copain Justin vit dans une banane tout près de lui. Un jour, Charles alla voir Gertrude la mouche. Gertrude donne des cours de conduite. Charles et Justin jouèrent un tour à Gertrude. Charles avait un moniteur sur lui, alors Justin pouvait communiquer avec lui. Tout allait bien jusqu'à ce que Gertrude découvrît le mystère. Soudainement, Charles perdit le contrôle, alors il n'a jamais réussit son permis de conduite. À son centième essai, il abandonna.

Rachel Haché, 11 ans, Beresford, NB
Carrefour Étudiant

Que c'est drôle quand je vais sur la lune avec les martiens, je me
promène dans la brume. J'invite mes amis, plus on est de fous,
plus on rit. Sur la lune, tout le monde est content, personne n'est
méchant. Si j'avais le choix, j'irais vivre sur la lune avec mon
chien et sa petite queue brune. Les martiens sont plus beaux que
l'on dit. Ils sont plein de couleurs vives, ça donne envie de vivre.
Les martiens, eux aussi, ont de petits chiens. La lune, c'est
comme une terre sans pollution. Ils ont une belle mer
pleine de poissons.

Olivier Hardy, 11 ans, Victoriaville, QC
École Vision School

Isn't it funny when scarecrows dance ballet at night when everyone is sleeping. They slip on their tights and tie on their ballet slippers and away they go dancing and prancing. With the cat singing opera and the cow playing the cello nothing could go wrong except the Tom cats bellow. But then ... in come five black crows dressed in pink tuxedos. They shadow over the land and stroll right up to the frightened scarecrow, not a sound can be heard. Suddenly! the leader cries out; " Can we dance too?" The scarecrow replies, " Sure" Everyone cheers happily. Isn't that funny?

Christina Harper, 10

Isn't it funny when scarecrows dance ballet at night, when everyone is sleeping. They slip on their tights and tie on their ballet slippers, and away they go, dancing and prancing. With the cat singing opera, and the cow playing the cello, nothing could go wrong except the Tomcats below. But then… in come five black crows dressed in pink tuxedos. They shadow over the land and strolled right up to the frightened scarecrow. Not a sound could be heard. Suddenly, the leader cried out: "Can we dance too?" The scarecrows replied: "Sure!" Everyone cheered happily. Isn't that funny?

Christina Harper, Age 10, Three Hills, AB
Prairie Elementary School

Isn't it funny when you consider life? Why were you, or anyone chosen for this particular part to play? Why this body, these parents? why not her body or his life? Maybe you consider it in terms of watching a very small child explore life, develop a personality. Isn't it funny to watch them laugh, often at nothing at all? So whether you consider life as the beginning or as a part you play, or even both, isn't it funny?

Andie Hartshorne-Pople, Age 12, Toronto, ON
Birch Cliff Public School

Isn't it funny when the only time you lose control when you are bike riding is when there is an object right in front of you? You're enjoying nature, feeling the warm breeze, and talking to your dad when BOOM your bike ride is spoiled. Fire hydrants, poles, mail boxes, trees, and fences seem to come out of nowhere! My bike seems to get magically sucked toward these thingumajigs like a magnet. Time to head home and get the Band-Aids out. Maybe we should go for a walk next time...

Justin Heinrichs, 8

Isn't it funny when the only time you lose control when you are bike riding is when there is an object right in front of you? You're enjoying nature, feeling the warm breeze and talking to your dad, when BOOM, your bike ride is spoiled. Fire hydrants, poles, mailboxes, trees, and fences seem to come out of nowhere! My bike seems to get magically sucked toward these thingamajigs like a magnet. Time to head home and get the Band-Aids out. Maybe we should go for a walk next time…

Justin Heinrichs, Age 8, Calgary, AB
Roots/Trinity Christian School

Que c'est drôle quand au soccer les enfants jouent avec le ballon
spécial. À chaque fois qu'un enfant frappe le ballon, il monte
haut dans les airs. Il n'allait jamais en ligne droite. Un jour,
l'entraîneur a décidé qu'on n'allait plus l'utiliser. Mais, le ballon
est sorti du sac et a sauté haut dans les airs. Il a retombé sur
la tête de l'entraîneur et tous les élèves se sont mis à rire.

Patrick Herman, 8 ans, Ottawa, ON
Collège L'Odyssée

Isn't it funny when... A dog saves your party from becoming a complete disaster. Let me explain: Mom was organizing games when we heard a mew. Pumpkin, the neighbor's cat, had sabotaged the gifts and piñata and was heading with frightening speed towards the chocolate cake. We chased her unsuccessfully. She was feet from the cake. Woof! Pumpkin hair raised, turned. A large beagle with brown spots ran towards her. He leapt upon the table, jumped over the terrified cat and stood in front of the cake, looking triumphant, yet sweet. We rewarded the happy dog with a pork chop.

Laura How, age 12

Isn't it funny when a dog saves your party from becoming a complete disaster. Let me explain. Mom was organizing games when we heard a mew. Pumpkin, the neighbour's cat, had sabotaged the gifts and piñata, and was heading, with frightening speed, towards the chocolate cake. We chased her unsuccessfully. She was feet from the cake. Woof! Pumpkin, hair raised, turned. A large beagle with brown spots ran towards her. He leapt upon the terrified cat and stood in the front of the cake, looking triumphant, yet sweet. We rewarded the happy dog with a pork chop.

Laura How, Age 12, Victoria, BC
Margaret Jenkins Elementary School

Isn't it funny when... you can't stop sneezing? One day Madison Taylor was walking, when suddenly, on Hullabaloo Street, she sneezed. She sneezed herself right home and took some Hysterically Good Sneezing Medicine. She jumped into bed and slept for ages. She had stopped sneezing! But when she went to the magic store on Hullabaloo Street she started sneezing again! When she left she stopped. Madison past Hullabaloo Street a lot to go to Hullabaloo School. Madison started to wonder; she visited the magic store again and found a mechanism to make people sneeze! That was the whole "Hullabaloo Mystery"!

Abigail Hudson   age 10

Isn't it funny when you can't stop sneezing? One day, Madison Taylor was walking, when, suddenly, on Hullabaloo Street, she sneezed. She sneezed herself right home and took some hysterically good sneezing medicine. She jumped into bed and slept for ages. She had stopped sneezing! But when she went to the magic store on Hullabaloo Street, she started sneezing again! When she left she stopped! Madison passed Hullabaloo street a lot to go to Hullabaloo school. Madison started to wonder. She visited the magic store again and found a mechanism to make people sneeze! That was the whole 'Hullabaloo Mystery'!

Abigail Hudson, Age 10, Omemee, ON
Grace Christian Academy

Isn't it funny when a sumo wrestler that is chubby, weighs five thousand Pounds and is very fat falls from the sky when you are walking down the street. He makes a big, big hole in the sidewalk. Then you look down into the hole and you notice that he is wearing a blue, sumo sized bikini. Then the sumo makes his home in the hole. He decorates it with another bikini, a hot tub, a television and carpets. He invites you over every day to watch football and have dinner. He makes spaghetti every night.

Keegan Hughes, age 7

Isn't it funny when a sumo wrestler that is chubby, weighs five thousand pounds, and is very fat, falls from the sky when you are walking down the street. He makes a big, big hole in the sidewalk. Then you look down into the hole and you notice that he is wearing a blue sumo-sized bikini. Then the sumo makes his home in the hole. He decorates it with another bikini, a hot tub, a television, and carpets. He invites you over every day to watch football and have dinner. He makes spaghetti every night.

Keegan Hughes, Age 7, Ajax, ON
Alexander Graham Bell Public School

99

Isn't it funny when an elephant falls out of the sky and lands
on you. Well, no it's not. It felt like a feather falling on me.
The elephant weighed two pounds. It happened to be a cloud
elephant. He took me to the cloud zoo. Where I walked around
and ate cloud popcorn. I took a ride on the elephant. We flew
really high. At the zoo, there was a red kangaroo. Suddenly,
I fell through a hole. I woke up, and it was all a dream. It was
funny and a little scary too.

Brandon Jacobs, Age 10, Kelowna, BC
St. Joseph School

Isn't it funny when someone is keeping a secret from another person who in fact already knows about the secret but who pretends not to know anything. The secret was a surprised birthday party. The whole family had decided to have a birthday party for Grandma Ly. According to the plan, my family had to take Grandma Ly shopping so that the others would have time to get things ready for the party. So, we took Grandma and Grandpa to Square One. But Grandpa already knew about the surprise, we were shocked. We realized that he had known all along.

Yunus Jawaheer, age 10

Isn't it funny when someone is keeping a secret from another person who, in fact, already knows about the secrct but who pretends not to know anything. The secret was a surprise birthday party. The whole family had decided to have a birthday party for Grandma Ly. According to the plan, my family had to take Grandma Ly shopping so that the others would have time to get things ready for the party. So, we took Grandma and Grandpa to Square One. But Grandpa already knew about the surprise. We were shocked when we realized that he had known all along.

Yunus Jawaheer, Age 10, Mississauga, ON
École René-Lamoureux

Isn't it funny when I awoke this morning to find myself covered in fluffy white fur with a cottontail and long ears. I'm a bunny rabbit. All I could think was how can I go to school looking like this! I heard my Mom call me for breakfast. I hopped downstairs. Mom saw me and said, "Who brought the bunny rabbit home?" No one answered Mom. I was so scared, I raced back to my bedroom to hide. Mom said, "Kelsey, wake up." I love bunny rabbits, but I was happy to find out I was myself again. The End!

Kelsey Kargus, Age 7

Isn't it funny when I awoke this morning to find myself covered in fluffy white fur with a cottontail and long ears. I'm a bunny rabbit. All I could think was how can I go to school looking like this! I heard my Mom call me for breakfast. I hopped downstairs. Mom saw me and said, "Who brought the bunny rabbit home?" No one answered Mom. I was so scared, I raced back to my bedroom to hide. Mom said, "Kelsey, wake up." I love bunny rabbits, but I was happy to find out I was myself again. The End!

Kelsey Kargus, Age 7, Haley Station, ON
Our Lady of Fatima School

Isn't it funny when time seems to come to a halt. Only a few minutes until the bell rings... only a few minutes until school's out. Those may be the longest minutes of your life. Isn't it funny when your grandparents always say how time flies... when it seems to be standing still. For a dog, does a minute feel like an hour? For a dragonfly, which only lives twenty four hours, does a day feel like years?

Use your time wisely, for even in the best of moments, some days you just want to spend time with your friends.

Michelle Karpman, 11

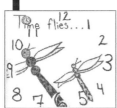

Isn't it funny when time seems to come to a halt. Only a few minutes until the bell rings... only a few minutes until school's out. Those may be the longest minutes of your life. Isn't it funny when your grandparents always say how time flies... when it seems to be standing still. For a dog, does a minute feel like an hour? For a dragonfly, which only lives twenty-four hours, does a day feel like years? Use your time wisely, for even in the best of moments, some days you just want to spend time with your friends.

Michelle Karpman, Age 11, Montreal, QC
Roslyn School

Isn't it funny when at exam time at school you get up too early? Last year at three o'clock Am when I got up to study, I decided to make my lunch early. I was so tired that I put Ketchup in my thermos instead of tomato soup. So I went to brush my teeth. I was still so groggy that I put hairgel on my toothbrush and toothpaste in my hair. I also used bubblebath instead of mouthwash. To cap it all, when I went upstairs to study, I was reading my dad's Driving Book instead of my Science

By Iqbal Kassam age, 11

Isn't it funny when, at exam time at school, you get up too early? Last year at three o'clock am, when I got up to study, I decided to make my lunch early. I was so tired that I put ketchup in my thermos instead of tomato soup. So, I went to brush my teeth. I was still so groggy that I put hair gel on my toothbrush and toothpaste in my hair. I also used bubble bath instead of mouthwash. To cap it all, when I went upstairs to study, I was reading my dad's driving book instead of my science!

Iqbal Kassam, Age 11, Vancouver, BC
West Point Grey Academy

Isn't it funny when your dog from China teaches you karate? My dog's from China and I taught him to speak English. I asked him if he knew karate.

He said, "Duh! I'm from China you know! If you take me to the pet shop and buy me lots of bones, I will teach you."

I said, "Ok."

We went to the pet shop. I bought him twelve bones, thirty frisbees and five hulahoops. I guess I have to teach him how to hulahoop. Sometimes I wish I never taught him how to talk!

Zoe Keirstead Age:10

Isn't it funny when your dog from China teaches you karate?
My dog's from China, and I taught him to speak English.
I asked him if he knew karate. He said, "Duh! I'm from
China you know! If you take me to the pet shop and
buy me lots of bones, I will teach you." I said, "Ok."
We went to the pet shop. I bought him twelve bones,
thirty Frisbees and five Hula Hoops. I guess I have to
teach him how to Hula Hoop. Sometimes, I wish I never
taught him how to talk!

Zoe Keirstead, Age 10, Lower Coverdale, NB
Lower Coverdale School

Isn't it funny when you get the
Ed. Zackary disease, everything
you touch turns into Ed. Zackary
what you want. Your sister bugs you
and you touch her and she turns
into the foot stool that you know
your dads going to use when he
gets home from work and you know
his feet REALLY STINK. When you
touch the grass and it turns into
a thousand pound smartie. When
your mom runs you a bath and you
touch the water and it turns into
a chocolate and marshmallow
smors. That is getting Ed Zackary
what you want.

Brittany Kelsall   9

Isn't it funny when you get the Ed Zackary Disease. Everything
you touch turns into Ed Zackary what you want. Your sister bugs
you and you touch her and she turns into the foot stool that you
know your dad's going to use when he gets home from work,
and you know his feet really STINK. When you touch the grass
and it turns into a thousand-pound smartie. When your mom
runs you a bath and you touch the water and it turns into a
chocolate and marshmallow s'mores boat. That is getting
Ed Zackary what you want.

Brittany Kelsall, Age 9, Surrey, BC
Boundary Park School

Isn't it funny when you imagine strange things? You can imagine a banana, all covered in bumps, you can imagine a camel with sixty-five humps. You can be an explorer, wearing a cowboy's hat, you can do anything, even be a cat, if you use your imagination! Imagination is silly stuff, you can be a gentle person or you can be rough and tough. But one thing's for sure, imagination's a thing you really need, or you'll be so bored, you won't even want to read! Isn't it funny when you use your imagination? It is, so imagine more!

Penelope Kerr, age 10

Isn't it funny when you imagine strange things? You imagine a banana all covered in bumps; you can imagine a camel with sixty-five humps. You can be an explorer, wearing a cowboy's hat; you can do anything, even be a cat, if you use your imagination! Imagination is silly stuff; you can be a gentle person or you can be rough and tough. But one thing's for sure, imagination's a thing you really need, or you'll be so bored, you won't even want to read! Isn't it funny when you use your imagination? It is, so imagine more!

Penelope Kerr, Age 10, Fredericton, NB
Liverpool Street Elementary School

Isn't it funny when Martians from pluto come to earth with Disguises on. when the martians took their masks of they looked like fruit cakes that had Big antennas over their heads. on the end of the antennas that were 3 feet tall Their eyes were very small. small as marbles They also had eye's on the Back of their heads that were hidden. The martians were coming to earth to get food because their food supply on pluto was very low. All they took was fruit and veggies. I could not believe they didn't take any chip's.

Jason Kowbel age 10

Isn't it funny when Martians from Pluto come to Earth with disguises on. When the Martians took their masks off, they looked like fruitcakes that had big antennas over their heads. On the end of the antennas that were 3 feet tall, their eyes were very small, small as marbles. They also had eyes on the backs of their heads, that were hidden. The Martians were coming to Earth to get food because their food supply on Pluto was very low. All they took was fruit and veggies. I could not believe they didn't take any candy or chips.

Jason Kowbel, Age 10, Lloydminster, AB
St. Mary's School

Isn't it funny when you think you're alone but really you're not. You have entered your grandmothers house and you find yourself in a strange haunted house. After standing in the same spot for awhile suddenly a goblin appears. He tries to convince you to come live here. I try to run to the door but I can't move, my hands get clamy and sweat beads appear on my forehead. Then POOF.... a fairy appears and tells me I have one wish. I think "oh please get me out of here" and "ZAP!" I'm in my own bed, Alone, thinking?

Jenna Kulka 10 years old

Isn't it funny when you think you're alone but really you're not. You have entered your grandmother's house and you find yourself in a strange haunted house. After standing in the same spot for a while, suddenly a goblin appears. He tries to convince you to come live here. I try to run to the door, but I can't move. My hands get clammy, and sweat beads appear on my forehead, then poof… a fairy appears and tells me I have one wish. I think, "Oh please, get me out of here," and, "ZAP," I'm in my own bed, alone, thinking.

Jenna Kulka, Age 10, Edmonton, AB
Sweet Grass School

Que c'est drôle quand je vais à l'animalerie et que je vois une souris entrer dans la cage d'un chat endormi. Ce qui est drôle, c'est que la souris fait des noeuds papillon avec les moustaches du chat. Quand je vais près d'une fontaine avec mon chien, il prend de l'eau dans sa bouche, fait la statue, crache l'eau, et c'est devenu lui la fontaine! Quand je vais chez mon amie, ses deux cochons d'inde se tiennent par les pattes, et dansent le tango! Quand je suis allée en Australie, un bébé Kangourou prenait une luciole pour lire le soir.

Laurie Labbé, 10 ans

Que c'est drôle quand je vais à l'animalerie, et que je vois une souris entrer dans la cage d'un chat endormi. Ce qui est drôle, c'est que la souris fait des noeuds papillons avec les moustaches du chat. Quand je vais près d'une fontaine avec mon chien, il prend de l'eau dans sa bouche, fait la statue, crache l'eau, et c'est devenu lui la fontaine ! Quand je vais chez mon amie, ses deux cochons d'Inde se tiennent par les pattes et dansent… le tango ! Quand je suis allée en Australie, un bébé kangourou prenait une luciole pour lire le soir.

Laurie Labbé, 10 ans, Dorval, QC
École Gentilly

QUE C'EST DRÔLE QUAND MES POISSONS se METTENT À CHANTER ET À DANSER COMME LES BEE-GEE'S AVEC UNE touffE DE CHEVEUX FRISÉS SUR LA tête. HÉ OUI, LE VENDREDI SOIR, LA BOULE DISCO TOURNE ET LE PLANCHER CHANGE DE COULEURS EN GARDANT LE RYTHME. Tout À COUP, UNE ÉPAISSE FUMÉE BLANCHE COUVRE RAPIDEMENT LA PISTE DE DANSE, LA MUSIQUE RÉSONNE DANS L'AQUARIUM PUIS, À TRAVERS LA FUMÉE ET LES JETS DE LUMIÈRE, ILS FONT LEUR ENTRÉE EN BALANÇANT LEURS NAGEOIRES DE BAS EN HAUT. QUOI, VOUS NE ME CROYEZ PAS ? ALORS DITES-MOI POURQUOI PERSONNE NE ME CROIT ?

SIMON LALONDE-CHARBONNEAU 11 ANS.

Que c'est drôle quand mes poissons se mettent à chanter et à danser comme les Bee Gees avec une touffe de cheveux frisés sur la tête. Hé oui, le vendredi soir, la boule disco tourne et le plancher change de couleurs en gardant le rythme. Tout à coup, une épaisse fumée blanche couvre rapidement la piste de danse, la musique résonne dans l'aquarium puis, à travers la fumée, et les jets de lumière, ils font leur entrée en balançant leurs nageoires de bas en haut. Quoi, vous ne me croyez pas ? Alors dites-moi pourquoi personne ne me croit ?

Simon Lalonde-Charbonneau, 11 ans,
Gatineau, QC, École primaire Mont-Bleu

Isn't it funny when I tried to sell my brother. My brother really gets on my nerves. He bothers me, he takes my stuff, he goes into my room when I'm not home, and he even ripped the pages out of my school textbook! I tried to sell him but... the Museum didn't want him, the Science Centre didn't want him, the Art Gallery didn't want anything to do with him, Ontario Place didn't need him... Do You Want My Brother?

Lara Lapchinsky, Age 10, Weston, ON
Westway Junior School

Que c'est drôle quand elles se parlent ! Les Sirènes-Des-Lacs font plein de bulles. C'est ce que j'ai appris dans mon expédition solitaire sur le lac Étrange. Je ramais calmement lorsque je vis des bulles. J'étais tellement appeurée que j'ai produit un cri bizarre sans le vouloir et les bulles s'estompèrent. Tout à coup, sept sirènes à la chevelure rouge sortirent leur tête de l'eau. Elles me regardaient avec un air surpris et elles me supplièrent de ne révéler leur existence à personne. Je leur promis, elles me remercièrent et replongèrent dans l'eau. Je retournai au chalet en cachant mon air rêveur.

Mylène Lapointe 12 ans

Que c'est drôle quand elles se parlent ! Les Sirènes-Des-Lacs font plein de bulles. C'est ce que j'ai appris dans mon expédition solitaire sur le Lac Étrange. Je ramais calmement lorsque je vis des bulles. J'étais tellement appeurée que j'ai produit un cri bizarre sans le vouloir et les bulles s'estompèrent. Tout à coup, sept sirènes à la chevelure rouge sortirent leur tête de l'eau. Elles me regardaient avec un air surpris et elles me supplièrent de ne révéler leur existence à personne. Je leur promis, elles me remercièrent et replongèrent dans l'eau. Je retournai au chalet en cachant mon air rêveur.

Mylène Lapointe, 12 ans, Terrebonne, QC
Collège Saint-Sacrement

Isn't it funny when dogs dance, but isn't it funnier when dogs talk. Isn't it funny when cats wear tutu's, but isn't it funnier when cats sing. But with all these funny things happening how can you ever not laugh. I'm telling you when you see these things happening don't try not to laugh, because if you do: you will be passing smiles onto more people. Make them smile or laugh too, you have to laugh even if it is stupid.

Kerie Larson, 11

Isn't it funny when dogs dance, but isn't it funnier when dogs talk. Isn't it funny when cats wear tutus, but isn't it funnier when cats sing. But with all these funny things happening, how can you ever not laugh. I'm telling you, when you see these things happening, don't try not to laugh because if you do, you will be passing smiles onto more people. Make them smile or laugh too; you have to laugh, even if it is stupid.

Kerie Larson, Age 11, Grande Prairie, AB
Swanavon School

Que c'est drôle quand une petite taupe perd ses lunettes. La taupe commence par chercher dans son blouson et dans les poches de son pantalon, pas de lunettes. Alors, un peu affolée, elle regarde dans ses tiroirs, ses armoires, sur les étagères, sur les bureaux. Où sont passées ses lunettes ? Fâchée, elle va au divan, soulève les coussins, regarde sous le téléviseur. Ses lunettes ont disparu ! Furieuse, la taupe casse sa vaisselle, déchire ses draps, brise ses cadres, arrache son tapis. Finalement, elle s'aperçoit dans son miroir et dit : « Les voilà mes lunettes. Sur le bout de mon nez ! »

Salomé Lavoie, 9 ans, Waterville, QC
École La Passerelle

Isn't it funny when you want something really badly, but when you get it, you aren't that happy? For instance, there was a girl who wanted a pony so much that she would trade her older sister for one. Next morning, there was a pony in her backyard. She was delighted. She rode the pony and played with her until she got bored. Suddenly, she realized that her sister no longer existed. Good thing this was only a dream. She liked the pony, but having a sister was way better. I guess not everything you desire can make you happy.

Tam Le   13

Isn't it funny when you want something really badly, but when you get it, you aren't that happy? For instance, there was a little girl who wanted a pony so much that she would trade her older sister for one. One morning, there was a pony in her backyard. She was delighted. She rode the pony and played with her until she got bored. Suddenly, she realized that her sister no longer existed. Good thing this was only a dream. She liked the pony, but having a sister was way better. I guess not everything you desire can make you happy.

Tam Le, Age 13, Brampton, ON
McCrimmon Middle School

Isn't it funny when somebody tells you hilarious jokes? Most people like witty jokes and love to laugh, from the heart. It usually makes people feel good and it gives them confidence. But did you know that humorous jokes can become serious or even ugly? There are some reasons that we shouldn't laugh too much, at people. It can hurt their feelings and they also lose their precious confidence. Also, it could cost you their friendship. I think that we shouldn't laugh at the expense of others! Rather, we should learn to laugh for joy, and celebrate life.

Kate Lee, 11

Isn't it funny when somebody tells you hilarious jokes? Most people like witty jokes and love to laugh from the heart. It usually makes people feel good and it gives them confidence. But did you know that humorous jokes can become serious or even ugly? There are some reasons that we shouldn't laugh too much at people. It can hurt their feelings and they also lose their precious confidence. Also, it could cost you their friendship. I think that we shouldn't laugh at the expense of others! Rather, we should learn to laugh for joy and celebrate life.

Kate Lee, Age 11, Surrey, B.C.
Heritage Christian School

"Isn't it funny when Your Aunty has jungle animals for servants? Max had never met his Aunty, she lived in India and he was going to visit her. Max gets off the plane and is met by Jake the camel who gives him a ride to Auntys. There he is welcomed by George the gorilla who stomps upstairs with his luggage, Prissy the peacock tells him that there is a snack in the kitchen for him. Max faints when he sees Midas the elephant putting peanut butter sandwichos on the table for him. Did I mention Max is a peanut."

Timothy Lefort 13

Isn't it funny when your Aunty has jungle animals for servants? Max had never met his Aunty, she lived in India and he was going to visit her. Max gets off the plane and is met by Jake the camel, who gives him a ride to Aunty's. There, he is welcomed by George the gorilla, who stomps upstairs with his luggage. Prissy the peacock tells him that there is a snack in the kitchen for him. Max faints when he sees Midas the elephant putting peanut butter sandwiches on the table for him. Did I mention Max is a peanut?

Timothy Lefort, Age 13, Stony Plain, AB
Millwoods Christian School

Que c'est drôle quand me mère se transforme en vedette. car les journalistes envahissent la maison, et je peux utiliser le téléphone pour parler à mes amis tant que je veux... Et elle ne s'en aperçoit même pas ! Mais après, quand on reçoit la facture du téléphone, elle s'en aperçoit un peu trop à mon goût... Mon père, lui, il se transforme parfois en distributrice de bonbons. Quand ça lui arrive, je me bourre la face... C'est drôle à voir. Mais quand c'est le temps d'aller chez le dentiste, ça devient un petit peu moins drôle... Ah! Pauvre petit eux...

Anaïs Légaré-Morasse, 10 ans

Que c'est drôle quand ma mère se transforme en vedette, car les journalistes envahissent la maison, et je peux utiliser le téléphone pour parler à mes amis tant que je veux… Et elle ne s'en aperçoit même pas ! Mais après, quand on reçoit la facture du téléphone, elle s'en aperçoit un peu trop à mon goût… Mon père, lui, se transforme parfois en distributrice de bonbons. Quand ça lui arrive, je me bourre la face… c'est drôle à voir ! Mais quand c'est le temps d'aller chez le dentiste, ça devient un petit peu moins drôle… Ah ! Pauvre petit eux !

**Anaïs Légaré-Morasse, 10 ans, Montréal, QC
École Saint-Ambroise**

Isn't it funny when you look out your window and animals are on parade. A blue pig flying and a red cow leaping. Then a purple dog hopping and a pink cat skating. Next a big green bear dancing and an orange horse twirling. I see a yellow llama bouncing and a gold monkey roller blading. I hear a copper frog playing the symbols and a silver sheep playing the saxaphone. I can't believe my eyes! Here comes a turquaise turtle driving a bus full of electric yellow zebras singing loudly. When the parade is complete. I can fall asleep.

Kaitlyn Legge age 9

Isn't it funny when you look out your window and animals are on parade. A blue pig flying and a red cow leaping. Then a purple dog hopping and a pink cat skating. Next, a big green bear dancing and an orange horse twirling. I see a yellow llama bouncing and a gold monkey roller-blading. I hear a copper frog playing the symbols and a silver sheep playing the saxophone. I can't believe my eyes! Here comes a turquoise turtle driving a bus full of electric yellow zebras singing loudly. When the parade is complete, I can fall asleep.

Kaitlyn Legge, Age 9, Cambridge, ON
St. Brigid School

Que c'est drôle quand j'entends ton rire, que c'est drôle quand je vois ton sourire, oui, toi, monsieur le clown avec tes ballounes. Qu'est-ce que tu peux me faire rire avec tes chaussons et ton capuchon. Oui, toi, monsieur le clown et tes blagues, blagues nounounes. Oui, toi, monsieur le clown seul à être capable de mettre du bonheur dans ma vie. Lorsqu'il ne me restera plus que cinq secondes à vivre et que je verrai défiler devant mes yeux, les plus beaux moments de ma vie je me souviendrais que ce sont ceux que j'ai passé avec toi.

Gérémy Lepage   11 ans

Que c'est drôle quand j'entends ton rire, que c'est drôle quand je vois ton sourire, oui, toi, monsieur le clown avec tes ballounes. Qu'est-ce que tu peux me faire rire avec tes chaussons et ton capuchon. Oui, toi, monsieur le clown et tes blagues nounounes. Oui, toi, monsieur le clown seul à être capable de mettre du bonheur dans ma vie. Lorsqu'il ne me restera plus que cinq secondes à vivre et que je verrai défiler devant mes yeux les plus beaux moments de ma vie, je me souviendrai que ce sont ceux que j'ai passé avec toi.

Gérémy Lepage, 11 ans, Montréal, QC
École Saint-Paul-de-la-croix

Isn't it funny when an alien tickles himself to sleep with his nose? Well, I thought it was when I visited the planet Ranjslhok! Qwerrils are such peculiar creatures. They're always exactly seventeen feet tall, and get around by slithering on their fingers. Their highest jumper can almost jump two and a half millimeters high! Their favorite sport is Ardee ball, in which they try to swat a floating ball with their elbows into a giant plant called the Defilicus plant to score. If you ever come to my house, I'll teach you how to play!

Samuel Levac-Levey, 11

Isn't it funny when an alien tickles himself to sleep with his nose? Well, I thought it was when I visited the planet Ranjslhok! Qwerrils are such peculiar creatures. They're always exactly seventeen feet tall, and get around by slithering on their fingers. Their highest jumper can almost jump two-and-a-half millimetres high! Their favorite sport is Ardee ball, in which they try to swat a floating ball with their elbows, into a giant plant called the Delificus plant to score. If you ever come to my house, I'll teach you how to play!

Samuel Levac-Levey, Age 11, Montreal, QC
St. George's School

Que c'est drôle quand maman fait des dégâts. Elle échappe
et renverse tout accidentellement. On ne sait jamais la surprise
qui nous attend. L'autre jour, elle a renversé un plat de sucre
sur le comptoir. Je l'ai aidé à ramasser et j'en ai profité pour
en lécher. Je l'aime beaucoup ma maman.

Ianick Levesque, 7 ans, Edmundston, NB
École Notre Dame

Isn't it funny when a person can be poor in the morning, and rich at night. In the morning, he rides his bike from a broken down old shack to work at a restaurant, with minimum pay. He goes home after a hard day and at night, he becomes a billionaire. He has his own limo, his own mansion, and everything he wants. He travels around the world in one night. Then, it's time to go to work again. On the way, he thinks to himself, if poor people have rich dreams, then do rich people have poor dreams?

Bo Li, Age 11, Richmond, BC
Kathleen McNeely School

Que c'est drôle quand la vie nous offre des blagues si drôles
que nous ne sommes plus capables de nous arrêter dc rire.
Ces blagues sont si hilarantes qu'on en pleure de rire. Cela
nous fait chaud au coeur quand on voit de jeunes enfants rirent
et s'amuser ensemble. Que c'est drôle quand le plaisir prend
place en nous et nous fait dire à quel point la vie est amusante
et comique. Alors, dites-vous que peu importe le métier que
vous faites selon votre choix, il faut toujours garder la bonne
humeur et l'humour dans la vie.

Joey Litalien, 10 ans, Sorel-Tracy, QC
École Laplume

Isn't it funny when you fall into another dimension? One morning, I woke up on a normal Sunday. I went downstairs and had breakfast. Then I decided to go biking. I got my bike, and off I went. About two blocks down, I saw a dark hole in the ground. Nobody else was around, so I decided to take a look. Suddenly, something bumped me and I fell into the hole. I found myself in my bedroom again. I went back to where the hole was. It was gone, but my bike was lying right where I had left it.

Geoffrey Littlewood, Age 12, Richmond, BC
T. Homma Elementary School

Isn't it funny when you come home
after feeding the dragons at the
zoo and you find your pet dinosaur
dressing in your mother's clothes!
My pet dinosaur, Dino loves to play
tea party, and wear my mom's
clothing. He is the best pet dinosaur
in the whole planet, and probably
the most fun. Sometimes, instead
of doing that we go out and fly
kites or ride bikes in the park.
At night we will take my magic
carpet out for a fly around the
universe. It is amazing. Sometimes
we may even stop for a snow-
cone on planet Jupiter!

Kaylie Lundgren, 13

Isn't it funny when you come home after feeding the dragons
at the zoo, and you find your pet dinosaur dressing in your
mother's clothes! My pet dinosaur, Dino, loves to play tea party
and wear my mom's clothing. He is the best pet dinosaur in the
whole planet, and probably the most fun. Sometimes, instead
of doing that, we go out and fly kites or ride bikes in the park.
At night, we will take my magic carpet out for a fly around the
universe. It is amazing. Sometimes, we may even stop for
a snow cone on planet Jupiter.

Kaylie Lundgren, Age 13, Stratton, ON
Our Lady of the Way School

Isn't it funny when Canadians say "eh"? Have you ever wondered why Canadians say "eh"? Well, I have and it could be because our favourite things begin with the letter 'A', but then, I guess we don't like cake, grapes or pies. We could say "eh" because were straight-A students, or because of Sir John A. Macdonald, our first Canadian Prime Minister. We could say "eh" because we are awesome, active and are amazing in an arena. Any way you look at it, Canadians are good, eh?

Mary Kate MacDonald, Age 10, Whitby, ON
C.E. Broughton Public School

Isn't it funny when... One morning my alarm went off, bellowing in my ear like an elephant. I looked at my alarm and knew I was late. I dashed downstairs. There was only time for toast. I burnt it extra black and crispy. I didn't have breakfast. I raced out the door. It was raining cats and dogs. I was halfway to school and just remembered I forgot my homework. I rushed back home. I looked at the calendar. Oh my goodness!!! It's Saturday!!! I started laughing hysterically. It was better than crying. Laughter is the best medicine of all.

Laurie MacDonell, 10

Isn't it funny when, one morning, my alarm went off, bellowing in my ear like an elephant. I looked at my alarm and knew I was late. I dashed downstairs. There was only time for toast. I burnt it extra black and crispy. I didn't have breakfast. I raced out the door. It was raining cats and dogs. I was halfway to school and just remembered I forgot my homework. I rushed back home. I looked at the calendar. Oh my goodness! It's Saturday! I started laughing hysterically. It was better than crying. Laughter is the best medicine of all.

Laurie MacDonell, Age 10, Winnipeg, MB
Robert H. Smith School

Isn't it funny when people say the bone in your elbow is called a funny bone? I don't know why they do, but they do. I don't know why they do because when I hit it, it isn't very funny. Actually, it kind of hurts. I still don't get it though, if it hurts and it isn't very funny when you hit your funny bone why do they even call it a funny bone?

by Keigan Mac Eachern age 8

Isn't it funny when people say the bone in your elbow is called a funny bone. I don't know why they do, but they do. I don't know why they do because when I hit it, it isn't very funny, actually, it kind of hurts. I still don't get it though. If it hurts and it isn't very funny, why do they even call it a funny bone?

Keigan MacEachern, Age 8, Trenton, NS
Trenton Elementary School

Isn't it funny when you dream
    about gremlins in your room?
How they pulled your socks and
    toys to the floor with a broom.
Your mom suddenly comes and
    tries to open the door.
She can't, there's too much
    stuff on the floor!
You hear her yell, "Clean this up now!"
It makes you jump in fright
    and say, "But how?"
She says, "You figure it out,
    you made this mess."
You think, "I didn't do this,
    I'll make those gremlins confess.
Then you remember, it was you
    and Benny Mocks
who had played with the toys and the socks
                Ryan MacLennan, age 11

Isn't it funny when you dream about gremlins in your room?
How they pulled your socks and toys to the floor with a broom.
Your Mom suddenly comes and tries to open the door. She can't,
there's too much stuff on the floor! You hear her yell, "Clean
this up now!" It makes you jump in fright and say, "But how?"
She says, "You figure it out, you made this mess." You think,
I didn't do this, I'll make those gremlins confess. Then you
remember; it was you and Benny Mocks who had played
with the toys and the socks.

Ryan MacLennan, Age 11, Vancouver, BC
Champlain Heights School

Isn't it funny when you and your best friend are going to dress up for Halloween and you are the same thing? One day a girl and her friend decided to dress up for Halloween. They both knew what they wanted to be, but didn't want the their friend to know. On Halloween they were going to surprise one another. So, the first girl dressed up like a beautiful black cat with a long tail. The other girl decided to be a beautiful black cat, as well. When they both reached the scary house, they laughed and laughed.

By Alicia MacNeil   Age 10

Isn't it funny when you and your friend are going to dress up for Halloween and you are the same thing? One day, a girl and her friend decided to dress up for Halloween. They both knew what they wanted to be, but didn't want their friend to know. On Halloween, they were going to surprise one another. So, the first girl dressed up like a beautiful black cat with a long tail. The other girl decided to be a beautiful black cat as well. When they both reached the scary house, they both laughed and laughed.

Alicia MacNeil, Age 10, Edmonton, AB
Our Lady of Victories School

Isn't it funny when ghosts fool around, and goblins bow down to the night; and witches fly round in a circle and down to the werewolfs that hide in the grass, and the werewolfs they howl, so ominously foul to the ear and to the soul, and the moon shines so bright that your sure it's not night, and the wind starts to whistle and blow. Then out of the night and out of the cold comes a wickedly ominous laugh and screaming and running I race to my house and jump head long into my bed! ha! ha!

Alexandra Manuel, Age 11

Isn't it funny when ghosts fool around, and goblins bow down to the night, and witches fly round in a circle and down to the werewolves that hide in the grass, and the werewolves, they howl, so ominously foul to the ear and to the soul. And the moon shines so bright that you're sure it's not night, and the wind starts to whistle and blow. Then out of the night and out of the cold, comes a wickedly ominous laugh, and screaming and running, I race to my house and jump head long into my bed! Ha! Ha!

Alexandra Manuel, Age 11, Chemainus, BC
Sunrise Waldorf School

Isn't it funny when dragons sneeze on Mars? All the Martians open their windows and yell "Hooligig" & "Bless you" in Mantian language). The yelling makes the dragons blush. Dragons are very shy. One day a young martian saw a pink dragon and said, "Hello, girl." The male dragon said, "Who are you calling a girl... My baby sister?" as his baby sister hopped out of his pouch. The baby and the Martian became friends. Later, the Martian sneezed. The dragon said, "Hooligig." The Martian turned pink and the dragon was never shy again!

Kate Martin   7

Isn't it funny when dragons sneeze on Mars? All the martians open their windows and yell "hooligig" ("bless you" in martian language). The yelling makes the dragons blush. Dragons are very shy. One day a young martian saw a pink dragon and said, "Hello girl". The male dragon said, "Who are you calling a girl… my baby sister?" as his baby sister hopped out of his pouch. The baby and the martian sneezed. The dragon said, "Hooligig." The martian turned pink and the dragon was never shy again!

Kate Martin, Age 7, Wroxton, SK
Calder School

Isn't it funny when I woke up on the moon. When I got there I saw a green alien and a purple cow on their honeymoon. They asked me what I was doing on the moon. I told them I wanted to go home. They brought me back to Earth in their spaceship. When I got home I told my mom and my dad all about what had happened. We all lived happily ever after.

The end.

Emily Mastragostino, Age. 7

Isn't it funny when I woke up on the moon and had no idea how I got there. Then I saw a green alien and a purple cow on their honeymoon. They asked me what I was doing on the moon. I told them I wanted to go home and they brought me back to Earth in their spaceship. When I got home, I told my mom and my dad all about what had happened and we all lived happily ever after. The End.

Emily Mastragostino, Age 7, Toronto, ON
Gosford Public School

Isn't it funny when...
a phone rings? You can't just leave it ringing. It's almost as if you have to pick it up. Plus you never know whoes going to answer. It could be your best friend, your worst enemy, or someone you love! It could be the worst phone call you could ever get. It could be the hospital calling, telling you your son or daughter has been in a tragic accident. Or it could be the best call ever! Either way, isn't it funny when a phone rings?

Brett A. McKernon, 12 yrs.

Isn't it funny when a phone rings? You can't just leave it ringing. It's almost as if you have to pick it up, plus you never know who's going to answer. It could be your best friend, your worst enemy, or someone you love. It could be the worst phone call you could ever get. It could be the hospital calling, telling you your son or daughter has been in a tragic accident, or it could be the best call ever! Either way, isn't it funny when a phone rings?

Brett A. McKernon, Age 12, Cochrane, AB
Manachaban Middle School

Isn't it funny when I go to my treehouse and see a funny old man sitting on a limb wearing a green suit, curved, floppy shoes, and a large, old black hat. I begin to laugh as he turned toward me and his long pointed nose hit a tree branch. He also had big ears. "What is so funny?" he spoke in a squeaky voice. Giggling, I said, "Who are you?" Dancing up and down, he smiled, "I have found the end of the rainbow." With a wave, he suddenly disappeared. With a yell, I see a pot of coins.

Dustin Meeks Age: 11

Isn't it funny when I go to my treehouse and see a funny old man sitting on a limb wearing a green suit, curved, floppy shoes, and a large, old black hat. I begin to laugh as he turned toward me and his long pointed nose hit a tree branch. He also had big ears. "What is so funny?" he spoke in a squeaky voice. Giggling, I said, "Who are you?" Dancing up and down, he smiled, "I have found the end of the rainbow." With a wave, he suddenly disappeared. With a yell, I see a pot of coins.

Dustin Meeks, Age 11, Harrowsmith, ON
Harrowsmith Public School

Que c'est drôle quand on s'imagine
que le gazon est rouge et que le
ciel est jaune. Que les chats
volent et que les oiseaux
nagent. Que l'on vit la nuit
et dors le jour. Que les fusils
font pousser des fleurs. Que les
jouets bougent et que les murs
parlent. Surtout que l'on puisse
se rendre à l'école dans notre
lit à roulettes tout en regant la
télévision. Mais avec beaucoup
d'imagination tout ceci est
possible.

Guillaume Melançon
7 ans

Que c'est drôle quand on s'imagine que le
gazon est rouge et que le ciel est jaune. Que
les chats volent et que les oiseaux nagent.
Que l'on vit la nuit et dort le jour. Que les
fusils font pousser des fleurs. Que les jouets
bougent et que les murs parlent. Surtout que l'on puisse se rendre
à l'école dans notre lit à roulettes tout en regardant la télévision.
Mais avec beaucoup d'imagination, tout ceci est possible.

Guillaume Melançon, 7 ans, Montréal, QC
École Saint-Fabien

Isnt it funny when you lose an eyelash and you make a wish and it comes true? Once there was a boy who kept losing eye lashes. He always made the same wish. A few days later he lost another eyelash. The wish didn't come True. A few weeks later he lost another eye lash. After a month he lost another eyelash. Again and again he wished. But the wish never came true. He asked his parents if they could get what he wished for. But they said no. Then, finally, the wish came true. He got a dog. Ending.

Ian Melanson, 8

Isn't it funny when you lose an eyelash and you make a wish and it comes true? Once, there was a boy who kept losing eyelashes. He always made the same wish. A few days later, he lost another eyelash. The wish didn't come true. A few weeks later, he lost another eyelash. After a month, he lost another eyelash. Again and again, he wished and wished but the wish never came true. He asked his parents if they could get what he wished for, but they said no. Then, finally, the wish came true. He got a dog.

Ian Melanson, Age 8, Dartmouth, NS
Portland Estates Elementary School

Isn't it funny when ice-cream falls from the clouds instead of snow and rain. So on a hot day you can eat it when its falling. Dessert people can eat it too so it won't be so hot for them. When it falls all kinds of flavors will be tasted like mint, strawberry, and orange. If your parents let you play in ice-cream, play in ice-cream. If not, too bad. For those people who are aloud, don't forget your winter clothes. So when the weather man says its going to rain, say yum because its going to rain ice-cream, Hurray.

Michael Melbourne, 9

Isn't it funny when ice cream falls from the clouds instead of snow and rain. So, on a hot day, you can eat it when it's falling. Dessert people can eat it too, so it won't be so hot for them. When it falls, all kinds of flavours will be tasted, like mint, strawberry and orange... if your parents let you play in ice cream. If not, too bad. For those people who are allowed, don't forget your winter clothes. So, when the weather man says it's going to rain, say "yum", because its going to rain ice cream. Hurray!

Michael Melbourne, Age 9, Kingston, ON
Bayridge Public School

Isn't it funny when you laugh? Your giggles make you fall
down and your heart jumps up and down and your brain
is empty? You roll on the ground holding your sides and
pounding the ground. Your mouth goes up
and down and it just keeps on going!
But best of all... YOU Cant Stop!!!
And the person beside you copies you and
the person beside him and him until everbody
is copying each other? Nobody can stop, not
one bit. Even if you had the blues now
you have the funnys? Isn't it funny?

Zahra Merali, 9

Isn't it funny when you laugh? Your giggles make you fall
down and your heart jumps up and down and your brain
is empty. You roll on the ground, holding your sides and
pounding the ground. Your mouth goes up and down and
it just keeps on going! But, best of all...YOU CAN'T STOP!
And the next person beside you copies you, and the person
beside him, and him, until everybody is copying each other.
Nobody can stop, not one bit. Even if you had the blues,
you now have the funnies. Isn't it funny?

Zahra Merali, Age 9, Corbiel, ON
Ferris Glen School

Isn't it funny when children go to Queen Elizabeth Public School which is a secret agent facility. Each grade would be a different level of training and each teacher would instruct us on a different ability. Mr. Cléroux would teach us martial arts and different fighting styles. Mrs. Gage would show us how to deactivate bombs and decode secret messages. Madame Bédard would instruct us how to use different transportation devices and Madame Kent would show us chemical reactions.

Q.E.P.S. actually means Quality Elite Private Spies!!!

Aaron Michaud, age 10

Isn't it funny when children go to Queen Elizabeth Public School, which is a secret agent facility. Each grade would be a different level of training and each teacher would instruct us on a different ability. Mr. Cléroux would teach us martial arts and different fighting styles. Mrs. Gage would show us how to deactivate bombs and decode secret messages. Madame Bédard would instruct to us how to use different transportation devices, and Madame Kent would show us chemical reactions. Q.E.Public School
actually means Quality Elite Private Spies!

Aaron Michaud, Age 10, Timmins, ON
Queen Elizabeth Public School

Isn't it funny when you swallow an acorn and it starts growing
out your ears. "Dad, can I use the saw to cut a few branches
off?" asked George. "No," said Dad. "We had better call the
weed man." "No, you'll kill me," said George. "Let's make a
shrinking machine and destroy the acorn," suggested George.
"Let's get started: screwdriver, wrench, bolt – finished!"
"In you go, Dad, to find the acorn," said George. "I am
in your tummy, one acorn destroyed," exclaimed Dad.
"No more swallowing acorns for me. Thanks, Dad!"

Logan Miller, Age 7, London, ON
Matthews Hall School

Isn't it funny when... you think about money? We make it, we save it and we spend it. Years ago you could go to the movies for a dollar. Now it costs about ten times as much. The cost of living has gone up and money does not buy as much as it used to. With easy credit, people abuse money and end up in debt. It usually leads to the poorhouse! I really don't want to go there! Here's the thing that I am wondering... We all know money doesn't grow on trees, then why do banks have branches?

Sarah Miller, age 12

Isn't it funny when you think about money? We make it, we save it, and we spend it. Years ago, you could go to the movies for a dollar. Now it costs about ten times as much. The cost of living has gone up and money does not buy as much as it used to. With easy credit, people abuse money and end up in debt. It usually leads to the poorhouse! I really don't want to go there! Here's the thing that I am wondering... We all know money doesn't grow on trees, then why do banks have branches?

Sarah Miller, Age 12, Bothwell, ON
John N. Given School

Que c'est drôle quand Éric est en scène! Le cinq Mars deux mille trois, après avoir tout préparé, la classe de sixième année présente son premier spectacle. Le professeur gère tout et a choisi comme personnage principal Éric, le gars le plus maladroit de la classe. Dès qu'il monte sur scène, les bêtises commencent. Il trébuche sur le rideau et l'arrache. Pouf!... Sur les deux premières rangées du public! Crac!... Écroulé le mur en carton! Boom!... Tombé l'éclairage! Aïe! Ouch!... Sur les autres acteurs! Quelle pagaille! Tout le monde panique! C'est un vrai cataclysme! Comme toujours, le spectacle, c'est Éric!!!

Trystan Millet-Verbecque   11 ans

Que c'est drôle quand Éric est en scène. Le cinq mars deux mille trois, après avoir tout préparé, la classe de sixième année présente son premier spectacle. Le professeur gère tout et a choisi comme personnage principal Éric, le gars le plus maladroit de la classe. Dès qu'il monte sur scène, les bêtises commencent. Il trébuche sur le rideau et l'arrache.
Pouf !...sur les deux premières rangées du public !
Crac !… écroulé le mur en carton ! Boom ! … tombé l'éclairage ! Aïe ! Ouch !… sur les autres acteurs ! Quelle pagaille ! Tout le monde panique ! C'est un vrai cataclysme ! Comme toujours, le spectacle, c'est Éric !

Trystan Millet-Verbecque, 11 ans,
St-Laurent, QC, École Katimavik

Isn't it funny when the mighty fall? Fluffy was a mighty cat. He was proud of many things. He was proud of his good looks. He was proud of his acrobatic stunts. He was proud of his bird catching. One day Fluffy saw a sparrow sitting on the open bathroom window. Suddenly he had a plan. Sneak up hop on the rim and then jump up on his prize. But he slipped on the rim and fell right into the toilet. Poor Fluffy wasn't fluffy anymore. Some people think even cats learn that pride comes before a fall.

Oles Mischena

11

Isn't it funny when the mighty fall? Fluffy was a mighty cat.
He was proud of many things. He was proud of his good looks.
He was proud of his acrobatic stunts. He was proud of his bird
catching. One day, Fluffy saw a sparrow sitting on the open
bathroom window. Suddenly, he had a plan. Sneak up, hop on
the rim, and then jump up on his prize. But he slipped on the rim
and fell right into the toilet. Poor Fluffy wasn't fluffy anymore.
Some people think even cats learn that pride comes before a fall.

Oles Mischena, Age 11, Toronto, ON
Josyf Cardinal Slipyj School

Isn't it funny when your socks go for a walk with your pyjamas and your headband jumps like a Slinky? OH! No! Look out the window, pencil and pen are running away. Your pants are playing soccer, your shoes are dancing and your teddy bear is watching television. Your homework was done but your eraser erased it. Your Kleenex is crying, your schoolbag is laughing. Your plate is singing, your bowl is bouncing, your cereal is splashing it's milk! Your video camera is not working. Your door is out of control! What will you do?
Just Giggle!

Shanda Mosher-Gallant 10

Isn't it funny when your socks go for a walk with your pajamas, and your headband jumps like a slinky? OH! NO! Look out the window; pencil and pen are running away. Your pants are playing soccer, your shoes are dancing, and your teddy bear is watching television. Your homework was done, but your eraser erased it. Your Kleenex is crying, your schoolbag is laughing, your plate is singing, your bowl is bouncing, your cereal is splashing its milk! Your video camera is not working. Your door is out of control! What will you do? Just giggle!

**Shanda Mosher-Gallant, Age 10, Summerside, PEI
Évangéline School**

Isn't it funny when those humans say "Hello." said little Molly Martian looking down from their space kraft. "Yes, it is." "Why don't they say greetings?" replied her twin brother Stu. Then their Mother walked in. "What are you two talking about?" "We're talking about how humans say hello instead of greetings." said Molly "oh it's just because humans are silly." said their Mother. "and your silly because you should be in bed now, come on!" "oh, do we have to?" "Yes now go brush your pearls!" So the little aliens went to bed still thinking about those silly humans.

Taylor Murray age -11

"Isn't it funny when those humans say 'Hello'!" said Molly Martian looking down from their space craft. "Yes, it is. Why don't they say 'greetings'?" replied her twin brother, Stu. Then, their Mother walked in. "What are you two talking about?" "We're talking about how humans say 'hello' instead of 'greetings'," said Molly. "Oh, it's just because humans are silly," said their Mother, "and you're silly because you should be in bed now. Come on!" "Oh, do we have to?" "Yes. Now go brush your pearls." So the little aliens went to bed, still thinking about those silly humans.

Taylor Murray, Age 11, Hamilton, ON
Bellmoore School

Isn't it funny when little kids say things they don't really mean? Once there was a little boy named Thomas. If I asked Thomas what color the sky was he would say red! If I asked Thomas what color the grass was he would say red! If I asked Thomas what color the sun was he would say red! If I asked Thomas what color a firetruck was he would say red!! Isn't it funny when you ask the right question and get the right answer?

Annie Nasato age: 8

Isn't it funny when little kids say things they don't really mean? Once, there was a little boy named Thomas. If I asked Thomas what color the sky was, he would say red! If I asked Thomas what color the grass was, he would say red! If I asked Thomas what color the sun was, he would say red! If I asked Thomas what color a firetruck was, he would say red! Isn't it funny when you ask the right question and get the right answer?

Annie Nasato, Age 8, Oakville, ON
St. Bernadette Catholic School

Isn't it funny when your mom decides to participate in Spring Cleaning? She storms through the house in a flurry of cleanliness, annihilating any mess that crosses her path. With her are weapons of mass destruction: brooms, mops, and Mr. Clean. This unstoppable force is not only lethal to dirt; let me warn you! Woe betide anyone who dares to set foot inside the house while she cleans! If you are caught, she might, dare I say it, put you to work! Nothing can save you from this horror. Let's just hope that spring is a long way off!

Erin Nelson, 13

Isn't it funny when your mom decides to participate in Spring Cleaning? She storms through the house in a flurry of cleanliness, annihilating any mess that crosses her path. With her are weapons of mass destruction: brooms, mops, and Mr. Clean. This unstoppable force is not only lethal to dirt, let me warn you! Woe betide anyone who dares to set foot inside the house while she cleans! If you are caught, she might, dare I say it, put you to work! Nothing can save you from this horror. Let's just hope that spring is a long way off!

Erin Nelson, Age 13, 100 Mile House, B.C.
100 Mile Junior School

Isn't it funny when you go up to someone and say hi and you get the cold shoulder, but it isn't because they're rude, it's because they're a balloon? That's what happened to me. I'm a bird. One day I was flying and spotted an orange bird. I flew up to say hi, but there was no answer. I thought it was very rude, so I gave it a tap on the back with my beak. Suddenly there was a loud BANG and I saw it fall to the ground. That's when I realized that the rude bird was a balloon.

Lynnea Ness, 11

Isn't if funny when you go up to someone and say hi, and get the cold shoulder, but it isn't because they're rude, it's because they're a balloon? That's what happened to me. I'm a bird. One day, I was flying and spotted an orange bird. I flew up to say hi, but there was no answer. I thought it was very rude, so I gave it a tap on the back with my beak. Suddenly there was a loud BANG and I saw it fall to the ground. That's when I realized that the rude bird was a balloon.

Lynnea Ness, Age 11, Edmonton, AB
Fraser Elementary School

Isn't it funny when you see someone miss a soccerball! Well thats what happend to me. It was a quiet day on Toothbrush Street. The little kids were laughing and the bullies were bullying!! This looks like a job for Miss The Soccer Ball Man! The only super hero that misses a soccer ball. He blows an enormous wind which hits his enemies. He walks up to the bully. Puts his ball on the ground, winds up, runs... and he misses. Sending a huge blow. Looks like the day is saved. all thanks to me.

Julian Newman 10 yrs

Isn't it funny when you see someone miss a soccer ball. Well, that's what happened to me. It was a quiet day on Toothbrush Street. The little kids were laughing, and the bullies were bullying! This looks like a job for Miss The Soccer Ball Man! The only superhero that misses a soccer ball! By missing that soccer ball, he blows an enormous wind, which hits his enemies. He walks up to the bully, puts his ball on the ground winds up, runs… and he misses, sending a huge blow. Looks like the day is saved! All thanks to me.

Julian M. Newman, Age 10, Pickering, ON
St. Isaac Jogues Catholic School

ISn't it funny when imaginations run away? I was walking down the street wondering what it would be like if animals were smarter than people.
I imagined a dressed pig standing by a people-pen watching a little girl rolling in the mud. Then I imagined a circus where an elephant was riding a man and a lion was the ring-master.
I imagined a zoo where a bear was taking a picture of a lady trying to paw a fish. Suddenly, I felt a tug on my neck, I looked behind me and realised my dog was walking me!

Cadence Newton   Age: 9

Isn't it funny when imaginations run away? I was walking down the street, wondering what it would be like if animals were smarter than people. I imagined a dressed pig standing by a people-pen, watching a little girl rolling in the mud. Then I imagined a circus where an elephant was riding a man, and a lion was the ringmaster. I imagined a zoo where a bear was taking a picture of a lady trying to paw a fish. Suddenly, I felt a tug on my neck. I looked behind me and realized my dog was walking me.

Cadence Newton, Age 9, Penticton, BC
Columbia Elementary School

Isn't it funny when the weather suddenly changes? First, the sun shines brightly in the clear blue sky. A red convertible cruises down the highway as a deep voice on the radio announces, "A downpour is expected this morning." The two occupants, a well-dressed man and woman, quickly pull over to raise the roof. As they struggle, dark clouds suddenly move in, thunder claps and rain pours down. Minutes later, the roof is up and the drenched couple are on their way. Suddenly, the dark clouds clear, and the sun shines brightly without a trace of rain. Isn't it funny?!

Keenan Ngo, 12

Isn't it funny when the weather suddenly changes? First, the sun shines brightly in the clear blue sky. A red convertible cruises down the highway as a deep voice on the radio announces, "A downpour is expected this

morning." The two occupants, a well-dressed man and woman, quickly pull over to raise the roof. As they struggle, dark clouds suddenly move in, thunder claps, and rain pours down. Minutes later, the roof is up and the drenched couple are on their way. Suddenly, the dark clouds clear, and the sun shines brightly without a trace of rain. Isn't it funny?!

Kennan Ngo, Age 12, Black Creek, BC
NIDES (North Island Distance Education School)

Isn't funny when an eraser plays tricks on students. One day, Sponge Bob threw his eraser. He threw it everywhere. The eraser decided to avenge itself. When Sponge Bob was doing his homework with his friend Patrick, the eraser decided to erase his homework. The next morning, Sponge Bob gave his homework to his teacher but there was nothing written on it. The teacher gave Bob a copy. The eraser laughed. Sponge Bob did his copy and the eraser erased it. When he gave his copy to the teacher there was nothing! Angry, Bob threw his eraser away!

Xuan Nam Nguyen, 12 years old

Isn't it funny when an eraser plays tricks on students. One day, Sponge Bob threw his eraser. He threw it everywhere. The eraser decided to avenge itself. When Sponge Bob was doing his homework with his friend Patrick, the eraser decided to erase his homework. The next morning, Sponge Bob gave his homework to his teacher, but there was nothing written on it. The teacher gave Bob a copy. The eraser laughed. Sponge Bob did his copy and the eraser erased it. When he gave his copy to the teacher, there was nothing! Angry, Bob threw his eraser away!

Xuan Nam Nguyen, Age 12, Montreal, QC
Sophie-Barat School

Isn't it funny when at my birthday party a magician hypnotized my cat into liking people food. When he snapped his fingers she was back to normal. One day my friend came over and pretended to be a magician. "Aloozkamazma" she said and snapped her fingers. Suddenly my cat got a strange look eyes and ran into the kitchen. Somehow she managed to open the fridge door and jumped in and ate everything. From now on we have a combination lock on the fridge and cupboards. Nobody's allowed to snap their fingers within hearing range of the cat

Rachael Nicholls age 11

Isn't it funny when, at my birthday party, a magician hypnotized my cat into liking people food. When he snapped his fingers, she was back to normal. One day, my friend came over and pretended to be a magician. "Aloozkamazma," she said and snapped her fingers. Suddenly, my cat got a strange look in her eyes and ran into the kitchen. Somehow, she managed to open the fridge door, and jumped in and ate everything. From now on, we have a combination lock on the fridge and cupboards. Nobody's allowed to snap their fingers within hearing range of the cat.

Rachael Nicholls, Age 11, Calgary, AB
Knob Hill Elementary School

Isn't it Funny When your French Fries are French and you can't understand a single Word their Saying? or When your Vegtables are on your plate and they have to many eyes, and they won't stop givving you dirty looks? that would be funny!? or When your Pizza's way to Saucy and it's calling you names of every kind? or Even When you Scream "Jumpin jelly beans" and The bowl of jelly beans hit the Ceiling! WOW! I Wouldn't stop laughing at that, or even the thought of talking Bookbags! That's when my whole life would end because of LAUGHING!!! ° ° °

Jessica Noftall Age 13.

Isn't it funny when your french fries are French and you can't understand a single word they're saying? Or when your vegetables are on your plate, and they have too many eyes, and they won't stop giving you dirty looks? That would be funny! Or when your pizza's way too saucy, and it's calling you names of every kind? Or even when you scream "jumpin' jellybeans," and the bowl of jellybeans hits the ceiling! Wow! I wouldn't stop laughing at that. Or even the thought of talking book bags. That's when my whole life would end because of laughing!

Jessica Noftall, Age 13, St. John's, NL
St. John Bosco School

Isn't it funny when the cows cluck and the chickens moo. I just love it when I hear the horses oink and the pig neigh. The farm is filled with awkward sounds every morning. "Oh no," I cried. "I am late for school." I had math, gym, science, and story time. In math learned soccer. In gym I learned two plus two. In science Miss. Rose read "Three Little Pigs." In story time I learned about magnets. When I came home I went straight to bed without doing my home work and I still got a A+.

Cailleach Noyes, 8

Isn't it funny when the cows cluck and the chickens moo?
I just love it when I hear the horses oink and the pigs neigh.
The farm is filled with awkward sounds every morning.
"Oh no!" I cried, "I am late for school." Today in school,
I had math, gym, science, and story time. In math, I learned
soccer. In gym, learned two plus two. In science, Miss Rose
read, "Three Little Pigs." In story time, I learned about
magnets. When I came home, I went straight to bed
without doing my homework and I still got an A+.

Cailleach Noyes, Age 8, Vancouver, BC
Grandview Elementary School

Isn't it funny when a purple turtle walks into your room? When one walked into my room, I kept it as my pet. I feed it purple peanuts eight times a day. When it is hungry, it laughs five times, then sings a song. I take it for walks twice a day. In the winter, I keep it in a room with red heat lamps, rocks, and water. I still feed it purple peanuts.

My purple turtle is the best pet ever! It really does deserve a name. So I think that I will call it Pinky Sammy Purple Turtle.

Alyssa-Mariya Ottema, Age 11

Isn't it funny when a purple turtle walks into your room? When one walked into my room, I kept it as my pet. I feed it purple peanuts eight times a day. When it is hungry, it laughs five times, then sings a song. I take it for walks twice a day. In the winter, I keep it in a room with red heat lamps, rocks and water. I still feed it purple peanuts. My purple turtle is the best pet ever! It really does deserve a name. So, I think that I will call it Pinky Sammy Purple Turtle.

Alyssa-Mariya Ottema, Age 11, Guelph, ON
Laurine Avenue Public School

Isn't it funny when something terrible turns into something wonderful. Anna had moved many times during her childhood. She was born in Iqaluit, moved to Hay River and then to Yellowknife. She ended up loving it there. Then Anna's parents announced that they were moving to Iroquois Falls in Ontario. Anna was devastated. Moving was difficult. Only one thing remained the same, Anna's great passion for figure skating. She practiced relentlessly. Over the years Anna's skills improved immensely. She competed in many worldwide competitions and became a world famous skater. As the old saying goes everything happens for a reason!

Shayla L. Pagonis , Age 13

Isn't it funny when something terrible turns into something wonderful. Anna had moved many times during her childhood. She was born in Iqaluit, moved to Hay River, and then to Yellowknife. She ended up loving it there. Then Anna's parents announced that they were moving to Iroquois Falls in Ontario. Anna was devastated. Moving was difficult. Only one thing remained the same, Anna's great passion for figure skating. She practiced relentlessly. Over the years Anna's skills improved immensely. She competed in many worldwide competitions and became a world-famous skater. As the old saying goes, everything happens for a reason!

Shayla Lauren Pagonis, Age 13,
Yellowknife, NWT, William McDonald School

Isn't it funny when we put the pizza dough that my **Nonna** made in the trunk of the car. Then my dad drove us all around town. My **brother** and I said, **mommy mommy** it smells like a pizzaria. After my dad parked the car. Then my mom opened the **trunk** and the pizza dough went all over her face. She came back in the car and looked **very** funny. My dad drove us home. This time he opened the trunk and **jess** what happened? The pizza dough was all over **him,** the trunk and floor. We couldn't make pizza.

Jessica **Paolino** age 7 ☺

Isn't it funny when we put the pizza dough, that my Nonna made, in the trunk of the car. Then my dad drove us all around town. My brother and I said, "Mommy, Mommy, it smells like a pizzeria." After my dad parked the car. Then, my mom opened the trunk and the pizza dough went all over her face. She came back in the car and looked very funny. My dad drove us home. This time, he opened the trunk and guess what happened? The pizza dough was all over him, the trunk, and the floor. We couldn't make pizza.

Jessica Paolino, Age 7, Montreal, QC
Michelangelo Elementary School

Isn't it funny when a pig
Swallows dynamite. Once a farmer
Owned a big pig. It was his
favorite possession. One morning
Bob the hog got loose. There
was blasting going on nearby.
The pig was very hungry
because he had Just missed
his morning munchies. He Saw
Some   yummy looking red things. Paying
no attention to the xxx's on
the box he gulped one down.
When a construction worker came
along   he found the pig chewing
on the dynamite. While he was running
to   tell   the   Others he heard
a large bang. I   guess It was
bacon   for   breakfast!

Maria Parker Age 10

Isn't it funny when a pig swallows dynamite. Once, a farmer
owned a big pig. It was his favourite possession. One morning,
Bob the big hog got loose. There was blasting going on nearby.
The pig was very hungry because he had just missed his morning
munchies. He saw some yummy-looking red things. Paying no
attention to the XXXs on the box, he gulped one down. When
a construction worker came along, he found the pig chewing
on the dynamite while he was running to tell the others he heard
a large bang. I guess it was bacon for breakfast!

Maria Parker, Age 10, Clive, AB
Lighthouse Christian School (F.L.T.) Homeschool

Isn't it funny when you get locked out of your house. So you have to climb in through the kitchen window. You land on the counter top with one foot in mashed potatoes and the other in the gravy. When you jump down off the counter top, you slip and fall face first into the dog's water dish. You get up and walk to the glass door and WHAM! You bang into it. You open the door, walk out, and shut the door behind you. Then you realize, you're locked out again!

Robin Peckford, 13

Isn't it funny when you gct locked out of your house. So you have to climb in through the kitchen window. You land on the counter top with one foot in mashed potatoes and the other in the gravy. When you jump down off the counter top, you slip and fall face first into the dog's water dish. You get up and walk to the glass door, and WHAM! — you bang into it. You open the door, walk out, and shut the door behind you. Then, you realize you're locked out again!

Robin Peckford, Age 13, Point of Bay, NL
L.P. Purchase Academy

Que c'est drôle quand on tourne.

Quand j'avais cinq ans, mon frère et moi jouions à cache-cache. Je me suis caché dans la sécheuse à linge et j'ai mis des vêtements sur moi pour ne pas être vu. Ma mère est arrivée! Elle a allumé la sécheuse à linge. Ça a commencé à tourner. Je me suis mis à courir à quatre pattes. J'ai crié de toutes mes forces. Ma mère m'a entendu. Elle est venue et elle a ouvert la porte. Je suis tombé. J'avais la tête qui tournait. Ma mère a commencé à rire. Alors, j'ai ri.

Joël Pelletier, 9 ans

Que c'est drôle quand on tourne. Quand j'avais cinq ans, mon frère et moi jouions à cache-cache. Je me suis caché dans la sécheuse à linge et j'ai mis des vêtements sur moi pour ne pas être vu. Ma mère est arrivée ! Elle a allumé la sécheuse à linge. Ça a commencé à tourner. Je me suis mis à courir à quatre pattes. J'ai crié de toutes mes forces. Ma mère m'a entendu. Elle est venue et elle a ouvert la porte. Je suis tombé. J'avais la tête qui tournait. Ma mère a commencé à rire. Alors, j'ai ri.

**Joël Pelletier, 9 ans Pohénégamook, QC
École St-Joseph**

Isn't it funny when you're Grandpa acts even younger than you? Well, mine does. His nickname is Rudy and he is a hyper seventy-year old, but he acts like he is only seven. Rudy's favourite possessions are his Siamese cat, Simon Henry, and his new speedboat. He also loves his Tony Hawk skateboard and he is "awesome dude". One time my Grandpa took out his false teeth and chased the paperboy around the block just for fun. Well, as the saying goes, "you're only as old as you feel". I guess that makes my Grandpa younger than me.

Adam Perri age 10

Isn't funny when your Grandpa acts even younger than you? Well, mine does. His nickname is Rudy, and he is a hyper seventy-year-old, but he acts like he is only seven. Rudy's favourite possessions are his Siamese cat, Simon Henry, and his new speedboat. He also loves his Tony Hawk skateboard, and he is 'awesome dude'. One time, my Grandpa took out his false teeth and chased the paperboy around the block just for fun. Well, as the saying goes, "you're only as old as you feel". I guess that makes my grandpa younger than me.

Adam Perri, Age 9, Brampton, ON
Robert J. Lee Public School

Que c'est drôle quand Sylvie fait un jardin. Elle plante des laitues qui se font aussitôt manger par les lièvres. Sylvie met des choux mais ceux-ci se font voler par le voisin. Elle sème du maïs pour montrer comment celui-ci pousse. Tout va pour le mieux, jusqu'au jour où elle découvre des vers blancs! Sylvie court acheter un produit contre les vers. Elle en étend sur le jardin. Les jours passent et ils sont encore là. Elle montre le potager à son mari et il éclata de rire, car les vers blancs étaient les grains de l'épi du maïs.

Amélie Pettigrew 11 ans

Que c'est drôle quand Sylvie fait un jardin. Elle plante des laitues qui se font aussitôt manger par les lièvres. Sylvie met des choux, mais ceux-ci se font voler par le voisin. Elle sème du maïs pour montrer comment celui-ci pousse. Tout va pour le mieux, jusqu'au jour où elle découvre des vers blancs. Sylvie court acheter un produit contre les vers. Elle en étend sur le jardin. Les jours passent et ils sont encore là. Elle montre le potager à son mari et il éclata de rire, car les vers blancs étaient les grains de l'épi du maïs.

Amélie Pettigreu, 11 ans, Trois-Rivières, QC
Collège Marie-de-l'Incarnation

Isn't it funny when cats purr? It's really not purring at all. When you hear it, you actually hear a radio signal from an unknown planet — Catopia. I got to go there once. It started when I saw my cat run across my yard. I had been looking for her, so I followed her through a grove of cedar trees. I saw her sitting in a small capsule. I jumped in too, and WHAM! I was on Catopia. Mice slaved for cats, and guards were watching them. I didn't like Catopia, so I jumped back in the space capsule, and went home.

Janae Pham Age 9

Isn't it funny when cats purr? It's really not purring at all. When you hear it, you actually hear a radio signal from an unknown planet — Catopia. I went there once. It started when I saw my cat run across my yard. I had been looking for her, so I followed her through a grove of cedar trees. I saw her sitting in a small capsule. I jumped in too and, WHAM, I was on Catopia. Mice slaved for cats, and guards were watching them. I didn't like Catopia, so I jumped back in the space capsule and went home.

Janae Pham, Age 9, Kamloops, BC
Nechako Electronic Busing Program

Isn't it funny when your pet elephant devours your prize mosquitoes? I mean like who would have award winning mosquitoes? Seriously, and a pet elephant? My great, great, great grandpappy! Believe it er not. Award winning mosquitoes and a pet elephant. One day his elephant was in his backyard and was minding his own business when my great, great, great grandpappy's award winning mosquitoes came and bit him. Jesper that was the elephant's name, was disturbed by these blood sucking creatures. In self defence he sucked them into his mouth and swallowed. When my grandpappy saw this he shouted, "Aghhagahh!"

Alex Pingitore Age: 11 years

Isn't it funny when your pet elephant devours your prize mosquitoes? I mean, like, who would have award-winning mosquitoes? Seriously, and a pet elephant? My great, great, great Grandpappy! Believe it or not. Award-winning mosquitoes, and a pet elephant. One

day his elephant was in his backyard and was minding his own business, when my great, great, great Grandpappy's award-winning mosquitoes came and hit him. Jesper, that was the elephant's name, was disturbed by these blood-sucking creatures. In self-defense, he sucked them into his mouth and swallowed. When my grandpappy saw this, he shouted "aghaagahh!"

Alex Pingitore, Age 11, Oak Bank, MB
Springfield Middle School

Isn't it funny when somebody snores? Maybe your parents snore! They all sound different. Some sound so loud that even earplugs won't block it out! Others go loud and quiet and then it seems like the person's stopped breathing. Then a huge release of air comes alongside a groan. I wonder how some husbands and wives can stand each other's snoring. Maybe it grows on them. It is funny when the person snoring doesn't know it. They wake up not knowing that you barely slept. Then they ask, "Have a good sleep?" You yawn and lie, "Yes, how about you?"

Emma Pipes, age 12

Isn't it funny when somebody snores? Maybe your parents snore! They all sound different. Some sound so loud that even earplugs won't block it out! Others go loud and quiet, and then it seems like the person's stopped breathing. Then, a huge release of air with a groan comes. I wonder how some husbands and wives can stand each other's snoring. Maybe it grows on them. It is funny when the person snoring doesn't know it. They wake up not knowing that you barely slept. Then they ask, "Have a good sleep?" You yawn and lie, "Yes, how about you?"

Emma Pipes, Age 12, Guelph, ON
College Avenue Public School

Isn't it funny when your mind thinks about silly things. I think gravity should depend on your behaviour. If you behave wrongly, you would have to do something nice to get back to normal. For example, you get angry in the morning and, instead of walking to school, you trip and fall. Then your friends laugh at you and they fly into outer space. You feel sorry for them and you can stand up. They are sorry and they come back to earth. If this really happened, I think everybody would learn a good lesson.

Claudia Pisarek, Age 9, Coquitlam, BC
Traditional Learning Academy

Isn't it funny when you think about sneezing? Sometimes I sneeze so hard that I think I might go zooming across a galaxy or two. Then, I would land on some weird planet and have to use my sneeze power to return back to Earth. Once I got back home, I would try to figure out a way of harnessing the awesome power of my sneeze. Then I would invent sneeze-powered boats, sneeze-powered cars, and even sneeze-powered trains. I could change the world with SNEEZE POWER! Now, isn't it funny when you think about sneezing?

Alexander Poirier   12

Isn't it funny when you think about sneezing? Sometimes, I sneeze so hard that I think I might go zooming across a galaxy or two. Then, I would land on some weird planet and have to use my sneeze power to return back to Earth. Once I got back home, I would try to figure out a way of harnessing the awesome power of my sneeze. Then, I would invent sneeze-powered boats, sneeze-powered cars, and even sneeze-powered trains. I could change the world with SNEEZE POWER! Now, isn't it funny when you think about sneezing?

Alexander Poirier, Age 12, Ottawa, ON
St. Clare Catholic School

Isn't it funny when people compare you to an animal when they are trying to say that you are good at something. My dad says I swim like a fish. I'm a little worried about swimming in the lake in case I look too much like a fish and somebody tries to catch me. My mom says that my brother is quick like a bunny but he doesn't like to eat carrots or cabbage. My friend Mirella is as fast as a cheetah but there are no wildebeest around here so she has to be satisfied with chicken fingers.

Sarah Pomedli, age 9

Isn't it funny when people compare you to an animal when they are trying to say that you are good at something. My Dad says I swim like a fish. I'm a little worried about swimming in the lake in case I look too much like a fish and somebody tries to catch me. My mom says that my brother is quick like a bunny, but he doesn't like to eat carrots or cabbage! My friend Mirella is as fast as a Cheetah, but there are no wildebeest around here, so she has to be satisfied with chicken fingers.

Sarah Pomedli, Age 9, West Porters Lake, NS
O'Connell Drive Elementary School

Isn't it funny when someone tells you a joke but it's actually
happening. Whenever the ugly green joke monster appears,
jokes come to life. However, the joke monster always turns
them evil and only supreme Seth can stop him. Seth suddenly
appears, "Bye Bye you evil monster, Supreme Power!" shouts
Seth, and he transforms. His powers are… fireball, lightening
strike and shield. Here comes some lightening. "Lightening
strike trap." Yeah, the monster is hit. Joke monster throws
a punch, but Seth uses his shield. "Combine powers," yells Seth.
"Fire strike trap." The monster vanishes. Now, the joke world
is safe again.

Seth Privitera, Age 7, London, ON
Centennial Central School

Isn't it funny when your hamster gets famous. Nicoe hamstar is a famous and talented hamster in hammy town. Nicoe is a circus gymnast he can do flips, cartwheels and walk a tightrope. He got famous back when he was a baby. Nicoe was interested in gymastics and wanted to perform. But his family was poor. One day he entered a contest. The best gymnast wins $4000 dollars. Nicoe was practicing day and night for a week. Tomorrow was the big day. Nicoe was ready. He performed his floor routine without any mistakes. He won the contest and the money.

Rachel Purvis, 9

Isn't it funny when your hamster gets famous? Nicoe hamster is a famous and talented hamster from hammy town. Nicoe is a circus gymnast. He can do flips, cartwheels and walk a tightrope. He got famous back when he was a baby. Nicoe was interested in gymnastics and wanted to perform, but his family was poor. One day, he entered a contest. The best gymnast wins $4000.00 dollars. Nicoe was practicing day and night for a week. Tomorrow was the big day. Nicoe was ready. He performed his floor routine without any mistakes. He won the contest and the money.

Rachel Purvis, Age 9, Toronto, ON
St. Fidelis School

Isn't it funny when aliens visit Earth? Their names were Kronx and Tronx. One day, they decided to visit Earth. "Kronx, with our superior intellect, we can rule Earth. But we need to find the leader," said Tronx. While searching for the leader the aliens spied a wealthy man sleeping with a teddy bear. "Tronx this specimen is surrounded by wealth, it must be the leader." Without warning, Kronx snatched the teddy bear. After probing the teddy bear, the aliens became exasperated. "This specimen withstanded our strongest weaponery," said Kronx. "Forgive us. We will never return." And they never did.

Crislana Rafael, age 12

Isn't it funny when aliens visit Earth? Their names were Kronx and Tronx. One day, they decided to visit Earth. "Kronx, with our superior intellect, we can rule Earth. But we need to find the leader," said Tronx. While searching for the leader, the aliens spied a wealthy man sleeping with a teddy bear. "Tronx, this specimen is surrounded by wealth, it must be the leader." Without warning, Kronx snatched the teddy bear. After probing the teddy bear, the aliens became exasperated. "This specimen withstood our strongest weaponry," said Kronx. "Forgive us. We will never return." And they never did.

Crislana Rafael, Age 12, Surrey B.C.
Ecole Simon Cunningham

Isn't it funny when you wake up at seven and the school bus comes at eight-twenty and you end up chasing it? You're running and yelling at it but it won't stop. Finally you get the bus to stop and you realize you forgot your backpack. So then you're thinking here I go again. Luckily Mom is running for the bus with your backpack. You yell to the driver stop, stop! Screeech! You get your backpack, get back on, and relax. Then you get to class and realize you don't have your lunch. Here I go again. MOM!

Kellan Rankin, Age:8

Isn't it funny when you wake up at seven and the school bus comes at eight-twenty and you end up chasing it? You're running and yelling at it but it won't stop. Finally, you get to the bus to stop and you realize you forgot your backpack, so then you're thinking, 'Here I go again.' Luckily, Mom is running for the bus with your backpack. You yell to the driver, "Stop, stop!" Screech! You get your backpack, get back on, and relax. Then, you get to class and realize you don't have your lunch. Here I go again. "Mom!"

Kellan Rankin, Age 8, Ormstown, QC
Ormstown Elementary School

Isn't it funny when you imagine about the first day of school. I imagine a monster coming into my classroom and saying he is my teacher for the rest of the year because he ate my real teacher! The monster is big and green with just a little bit of yellow. He has three eyes, four nostrils, five belly buttons and he smells like pumpernickle bread chewed up bubble gum and chalk dust - Eww he smells! Imagine all the kids running away to talk to the principal about this but she is missing too! Now wouldn't that be funny?

Katie Reich age: 11

Isn't it funny when you imagine about the first day of school. I imagine a monster coming into my classroom and saying he is my teacher for the rest of the year because he ate my real teacher! The monster is big and green with just a little bit of yellow. He has three eyes, four nostrils, five belly buttons, and he smells like pumpernickel bread, chewed up bubble gum, and chalk dust. Eww, he smells! Imagine all the kids running away to talk to the principal about this, but she is missing too! Now wouldn't that be funny?

Katie Reich, Age 11, Kirkland, QC
St. Paul Elementary School

*Isn't it funny when you're terrified
by your best friend during the silence
of a foggy night? Peeking through
my blinds I froze. I saw a spooky,
enormous black figure pacing
back and forth with a gaping mouth,
fangs, and claws. Ready to scream
for help and run for my life something
powerful held me back as I gaped in
awe at the strength in this beast.
As I stared in terror, reassurance
slowly flowed through my veins.
Comprehending that this imposing
creature was my friendly, cuddly,
and playful dog Gem. I was able
to lay down again in peace.*

11yrs.   Brennan Richards

Isn't it funny when you're terrified by your best friend during
the silence of a foggy night? Peeking through my blinds, I froze.
I saw a spooky, enormous black figure pacing back and forth with
a gaping mouth, fangs, and claws. Ready to scream for help and
run for my life, something powerful held me back as I gaped in
awe at the strength in this beast. As I stared in terror, reassurance
slowly flowed through my veins. Comprehending that this
imposing creature was my friendly, cuddly, and playful
dog Gem. I was able to lay down again in peace.

Brennan Richards, Age 11, King City, ON
Springhill Academy

Isn't it funny when you arrive at school and your best friend has a zit on her nose. The zit is big reddish-brown and terribly ugly. You gather all your friends to see Godzitla the zit. Your principal wonders what all the noise is. She comes over. Fortunately she has her camera and snaps a photo of Godzitla for the newsletter. Your best friend is totally embarrased because everyone is laughing. You laugh as well. Suddenly you feel something funny on your forehead. Yikes! a huge zit! Everyone laughs and it's not so funny anymore. Oops, your turn.

Jade Richardson   11

Isn't it funny when you arrive at school and your best friend
has a zit on her nose. The zit is big, reddish brown, and terribly
ugly. You gather all your friends to see 'Godzitla the zit'.
Your principal wonders what all the noise is. She comes over.
Fortunately, she has her camera and snaps a photo of Godzitla
for the newsletter. Your best friend is totally embarrassed
because everyone is laughing. You laugh as well. Suddenly,
you feel something funny on your forehead. Yikes! A huge zit!
Everyone laughs, and it's not so funny anymore. Oops, your turn.

Jade Richardson, Age 11, Nanaimo, BC
Pauline Haarer School

Isn't it funny when you think about how people used to think? Long ago, people thought the world was flat, imagine that! And can you believe they thought the moon was made of cheese, oh please! They even thought the sun went around the Earth, and when they found out how it really worked — oh the talk around the hearths! Then if you fell and cut your knee they would rub mud into it you see. But then again.....just imagine what people might say one day about how we think today.

Halley D. Roache, Age 10

Isn't it funny when you think about how people used to think? Long ago, people thought the world was flat, imagine that! And, can you believe, they thought the moon was made of cheese, oh please! They even thought the sun  went around the Earth, and when they found out how it really worked – oh, the talk around the hearths! Then, if you fell and cut your knee, they would rub mud into it, you see. But, then again... just imagine what people might say one day about how we think today.

Halley D. Roache, Age 10, Bridgewater, NS
Bridgewater Elementary School

Isn't it funny when you go to the doctor's office and they give you one of those silly johnny shirts. You head to the changing room, which is on the other side of the packed waiting room, to put on your embarrassing johnny shirt that is wide open in the back and held together by the puniest, weakest threads you can imagine! You soon realize there's no coverup but since you're already late, you quickly tiptoe into the waiting room. Everyone starts laughing and giggling out loud when you realize it was the ONE day you didn't wear your TIGHTY WHITIES!

Patrick Ross, 9 yrs.

Isn't it funny when you go to the doctor's office and they give you one of those silly Johnny shirts. You head to the changing room, which is on the other side of the packed waiting room, to put on your embarrassing Johnny shirt that is wide open in the back, and held together by the puniest, weakest threads you can imagine! You soon realize there's no cover-up, but since you're already late, you quickly tiptoe into the waiting room. Everyone starts laughing and giggling out loud when you realize it was the ONE day you didn't wear your TIGHTY WHITIES.

Patrick Ross, Age 9, Truro, NS
Douglas Street Elementary School

Isn't it funny when... Hockey equipment becomes it's own Wayne Gretzky? Your parents buy you brand new hockey equipment, and you put it all on and you become someone else. You get on the ice, and you can skate as fast as the speed of light, and you can shoot a puck directly through the boards! All your coaches see you play, and tell you that you should be trying out for the National Hockey League! You arrive at the National Hockey League tryouts and you see all these hockey players like Joe Sakic and Mario Lemieux. If life were like that ...

Daniel Sager age 12

Isn't it funny when hockey equipment becomes its own Wayne Gretzky? Your parents buy you brand new hockey equipment, and you put it all on and become someone else. You get on the ice, and you skate as fast as the speed of light, and you can shoot a puck directly through the boards! All your coaches see you play and tell you that you should be trying out for the National Hockey League! You arrive at the National Hockey League tryouts and you see all these hockey players like Joe Sakic and Mario Lemieux. If life were like that...

Daniel Sager, Age 12, Winnipeg, MB
École Julie-Riel

Isn't it funny when you see a talking dragon! Well I think it's funny. One day Diana was walking towards the grey castle. She walked down the bridge of lava. She tried to open the door, but she couldn't. She stood at the door for five minutes. After awhile a dragon showed up in front of her, he was really funny. Diana thought the dragon was silly and that he was friendly, he could talk too! Danny (the dragon) talked to Diana and she found out he was really nice. They were the best of friends.

Erica Saikaley Age: 9

Isn't it funny when you see a talking dragon! Well, I think it's funny. One day, Diana was walking toward the grey castle. She walked down the bridge of lava. She tried to open the castle door, but she couldn't. She stood at the door for five minutes. After a while, a dragon showed up in front of her; she was really funny. Diana thought the dragon was silly and that he was friendly; he could talk too! Danny (the dragon) talked to her and she found out he was really nice. They were the best of friends.

Erica Saikaley, Age 9, Manotick, ON
Manotick Public School

Que c'est drôle quand c'est maman qui ouvre, sourire aux lèvres, la porte grinçante, bordure de la nuit et du jour. Moi qui sortis alors du sommeil, bien pensant. Que c'est drôle quand c'est papa qui, bien joyeux, part encore une fois à bord de sa voiture au travail, d'ici aux confins de l'univers. Que c'est drôle quand c'est grand-mère qui prépare le dernier repas, pour ensuite voir arriver grand-père revenir de n'importe où. Que c'est drôle, je m'endors enfin dans ce lit devenu si seul, maintenant bien loin de notre ancien chez-nous. Que c'est drôle de vivre sur Mars...

Francis Sarrazin 12 ans

Que c'est drôle quand c'est maman qui ouvre, sourire aux lèvres, la porte grinçante, bordure de la nuit et du jour. Moi qui sortis alors du sommeil, bien pensant. Que c'est drôle quand c'est papa qui, bien joyeux, part encore une fois à bord de sa voiture au travail, d'ici aux confins de l'univers. Que c'est drôle quand c'est grand-mère qui prépare le dernier repas, pour ensuite voir arriver grand-père revenir de n'importe où. Que c'est drôle je m'endors enfin, dans ce lit devenu si seul, maintenant bien loin de notre ancien chez-nous. Que c'est drôle de vivre sur Mars…

**Francis Sarrazin, 12 ans, Saint-Jean Sur Richelieu, QC
École Chanoine-Armand-Racicot**

Isn't it funny when you ask a question to your little brother or sister and he or she understands something different or doesn't even understand at all! Like one experience that I have experienced was when my sister was little I asked her if she wanted peameal bacon with her eggs. And I guess she didn't know what peameal bacon was because she asked "What's the difference between female bacon and male bacon?" It was hilarious! Sometimes little siblings can be a pain in the butt, but my little sister always made me laugh ever since she was a baby!

Niki Sawni, 12

Isn't it funny when you ask a question to your little brother or sister and he or she understands something different, or doesn't even understand at all! Like one experience that I have experienced was when my sister was younger, I asked her if she wanted peameal bacon with her eggs. And I guess she didn't know what peameal bacon was because she asked, "What's the difference between female bacon and male bacon?" It was hilarious! Sometimes, little siblings can be a pain in the butt, but my little sister always makes me laugh ever since she was a baby!

Niki Sawni, Age 12, Richmond Hill, ON
Beverley Acres Public School

Isn't it funny when I dive under the water, only to discover a treasure chest containing three secrets. The first secret is in the shape of a mysterious, undiscovered fish. The fish opens and closes its mouth, giving out messages in code form. The second secret is a bright color I can barely look at because its secret burns my eyes. It is an undiscovered color that's never been named, and it is giving out thoughts. The third and final secret is amazing. It is an undiscovered gem that shines love. WOW! This is more than funny.

Keaton Schmidt, 7

Isn't it funny when I dive under the water only to discover a treasure chest containing three secrets. The first secret is in the shape of a mysterious, undiscovered fish. The fish opens and closes its mouth, giving out messages in code form. The second secret is a bright color I can barely look at because its secret burns my eyes. It is an undiscovered color that's never been named, and it is giving out thoughts. The third and final secret is amazing. It is an undiscovered gem that shines love. WOW! This is more than funny.

Keaton Schmidt, Age 7, Melfort, SK
Brunswick Elementary School

Que c'est drôle quand on apprend à marcher. On tombe sur les fesses à plusieurs reprises. Après ce qui semble être une éternité, on monte finalement sur nos petits pieds. On marche et on marche, on ne veut plus arrêter. On marche à travers la grande maison. Un jour on apprend à courir. On court à travers les villes, à travers les pays. On court bravement autour du stade olympique et on bat le record mondial. On court et on gagne des dizaines de médailles. On rentre finalement à notre très chère maison, pour enseigner à nos enfants comment marcher.

Sami Schroeder-Tabah, 12

Que c'est drôle quand on apprend à marcher. On tombe sur les fesses à plusieurs reprises. Après ce qui semble être une éternité, on monte finalement sur nos petits pieds. On marche et on marche, on ne veut plus arrêter. On marche à travers la grande maison. Un jour, on apprend à courir. On court à travers les villes, à travers les pays. On court bravement autour du stade olympique et on bat le record mondial. On court et on gagne des dizaines de médailles. On rentre finalement à notre très chère maison, pour enseigner à nos enfants comment marcher.

Sami Schroeder-Tabah, 12 ans, Chicoutimi, QC
École à la maison

Isn't it funny when, as a little boy, my parents left me at the zoo! I went over to the monkey cage to see what they could do. I spit at the monkey and he spit at me too. He got me in the eye, and I started to cry. The zookeeper saw me and took me for a walk, and during that time we started to talk. He called my parents on the phone to see if they were home. My parents came to get me, and the monkey came too!

Ryan Scott 13 yrs old

Isn't it funny when, as a little boy, my parents left me at the zoo! I went over to the monkey cage to see what they could do. I spit at the monkey and he spit at me too. He got me in the eye, and I started to cry. The zookeeper saw me and took me for a walk, and during that time we started to talk. He called my parents on the phone to see if they were home. My parents came to get me, and the monkey came too!

Ryan Scott, Age 13, Oxbow, SK
Oxbow Prairie Heights School

Isn't it funny when I tickle your wings! You laugh so much every time I tickle your wings. You try to say stop but you can't because your laughing so hard, when I tickle your wings! You try to run but before you have a chance I tickle your wings! You try to push away but you always end up laughing when I tickle your wings! But one day you caught me in the act and you tickled me back hard and I will never forget the day I was touched by an angel.
Dedicated to
my dad
Kerry Severson.

Melissa Severson Age 11

Isn't it funny when I tickle your wings! You laugh so much every time I tickle your wings! You try to say stop, but you can't because you're laughing so hard when I tickle your wings! You try to run, but before you have a chance, I tickle your wings! You try to push away, but you always end up laughing when I tickle your wings! But one day, you caught me in the act and you tickled me back hard, and I will never forget the day I was touched by an angel. Dedicated to my dad, Kerry Severson.

Melissa Severson, Age 11, Armstrong, BC
Len Wood Elementary School

Isn't it funny when you look back on the previous beliefs of mankind. The world was thought to be flat. Flying was out of the question. The breaking of the sound barrier could only be a dream. The moon was out of reach. Everything in today's ordinary room has things that people in the past couldn't even imagine. My great-grandfather said, in his day people didn't eat tomatoes. They were considered poisonous. This makes me think, how many true beliefs do we have today, that will be false tomorrow?

Joelle Sherman age 12

Isn't it funny when you look back on the previous beliefs of mankind? The world was thought to be flat. Flying was out of the question. The breaking of the sound barrier could only be a dream. The moon was out of reach. Everything in today's ordinary room has things that people in the past couldn't even imagine. My Great Grandfather said, in his day, people didn't eat tomatoes. They were considered poisonous. This makes me think, how many true beliefs do we have today that will be false tomorrow?

Joelle Sherman, Age 12, Toronto, ON
Cosburn Middle School

Isn't it funny when you're staring at the moon on a clear night and suddenly it smiles back at you? You do a double take but the moon's cheeks have plumped up as a grin stretches across its face. There's a twinkle in the moon's eyes and then you realize: the moon isn't supposed to have eyes! The moon uses its stretchy arms to scoop you up and sits you on top of a crater for the greatest vantage point there could be. You don't know if you're dreaming or delirious but it doesn't matter because you're giddy with happiness.

Kevin Shustack   Age: 12

Isn't it funny when you're staring at the moon on a clear night and suddenly, it smiles back at you? You do a double take, but the moon's cheeks have plumped up as a grin stretches across its face. There's a twinkle in the moon's eyes, and then you realize the moon isn't supposed to have eyes! The moon uses its stretchy arms to scoop you up, and sits you on top of a crater for the greatest vantage point there could be. You don't know if you're dreaming or delirious, but it doesn't matter because you're giddy with happiness.

Kevin Shustack, Age 12, Montreal, QC
Bialik School

Isn't it funny when frogs leap toward you, playing their striped kazoos?
They hop up and down and all around, causing a hullabaloo.
Isn't it funny when you see fat hippos, wallowing in the mud?
The purple and green are hardly seen, while red ones shine in the sun.
Isn't it funny when blue baboons play ring around the rosie?
They topple down with thunderous sounds while picking up pockets of posies.
But it's not funny when you regain concentration to find it's all your imagination.
Then you stare with rage, at your empty page, and sigh with utter frustration.

Victoria Sirega age 11

Isn't it funny when frogs leap toward you, playing their striped kazoos? They hop up and down and all around, causing a hullabaloo. Isn't it funny when you see fat hippos wallowing in the mud? The purple and green are hardly seen, while the red ones shine in the sun. Isn't it funny when blue baboons play ring-around-the-rose? They topple down with thunderous sounds, while picking up pockets of posies. But it's not funny when you regain concentration to find it's all your imagination. Then, you stare with rage at your empty page, and sigh with utter frustration.

Victoria Sirega, Age 11, Kitchener, ON
Home schooled

Que c'est drôle quand on est une poubelle ! Mon parfum est tellement exquis ! La preuve, lorsque j'émane mon odeur, toutes les mouches du monde tournent autour de moi. Quand je laisse exhalter mon arôme, ils se précipitent sur moi comme si j'étais leur seul espoire de vivre. Je suis comme une super star. Les mouches et les abeilles sont les journalistes achalents. Des fois leur présence m'irrite énormement. Grâce aux humains, j'ai même une limousine à ma portée qui vient me conduire avec mes compagnontes jusqu'à ma coquette demeure : le dépotoire.

Haitham Souissi   11 ans

Que c'est drôle quand on est une poubelle ! Mon parfum est tellement exquis ! La preuve, lorsque j'émane mon odeur, toutes les mouches du monde tournent autour de moi. Quand je laisse exhalter mon arôme, elles se précipitent sur moi comme si j'étais leur seul espoir de vivre. Je suis comme une superstar. Les mouches et les abeilles sont les journalistes achalants. Des fois, leur présence m'irrite énormément. Grâce aux humains, j'ai même une limousine à ma portée qui vient me conduire avec mes compagnons jusqu'à ma coquette demeure : le dépotoire.

Haitham Souissi, 11 ans, Saint-Laurent, QC
École Secondaire Saint-Laurent

Isn't it funny when you're the only guy in the family, and the little girl dresses you up. Then, the mother wraps a pink kerchief around your neck. So, you look in the mirror, just out of curiosity, and decide that you actually look  pretty unique! The neighbours think it's unusual for a guy like me to wear a pink kerchief. Except, Ken claims it's a bandana, not a kerchief. Guys don't wear kerchiefs. Me, I don't ever want to take it off. Dazzling green eyes, ebony black hair, and a pink bandana. Sincerely, your 'Vogue Feline', Scrapper the cat.

Elizabeth Pearl Spearing, Age 10, Edmonton, AB
Victoria School of Performing & Visual Arts

Isn't it funny when your fruit and veggie platters come to life!? Just imagine you're at your school dance, and the Red Hot Chili Peppers begin playing the meringue when the mangoes come out, doing the tango. The banana was doing the splits, while the tomato was trying to "ketchup" with the green pepper to do the salsa. The peach and the plum rolled in, thinking they were a "pear". Mr. and Mrs. Potato couldn't keep the "beet", and the onion was crying because it didn't have a "date". The corn was stalking the baby carrots. Thank goodness for imagination!

Garett Stuckless, Age 11, Whitby, ON
C.E. Broughton Public School

Isn't it funny when humans talk about how they rule the world? How come we don't have a say in it? We Chickens outnumber them big time!

So I have a few questions... Why do we get stuck in these little fenced yards all the time, with no access to the internet? Where's our Kentucky Fried Human? And what's this obsession with chickens crossing the road?

We must take a stand! The time to act is now! Power to the chickens!

 Delaney Swanson, 12

Isn't it funny when humans talk about how they're ruling the world? How come we don't have a say in it? Us chickens out-number them, big time! So, I have a couple of questions... why do we get stuck in these little fenced yards all the time, with no access to the Internet? Where's our seat in Parliament? Where's our Kentucky Fried Human? And what's this obsession with chickens crossing the road? We must take a stand! The time to act is now! Power to the chickens!

Delaney Swanson, Age 12, Orangeville, ON
Princess Elizabeth Public School

Que c'est drôle quand tu me fais cette drôle de face. Cette face ressemble à un babouin. La face que tu me fais me donne la joie et le bonheur d'être avec toi. Ça remplit mon coeur pour un mois d'amour et de plaisir. Toi el moi on est comme des siamoises colées par la main. Pas moyen de nous séparer. Si quelqu'un nous sépare, mon coeur se brisera en miettes. Quand tu plisses le front et que tu sors la langue et que tu appuies sur ton nez ça donne TA FACE DE BABOUIN !!

Andréanne Tanguay 10 ans

Que c'est drôle quand tu me fais cette drôle de face. Cette face ressemble à un babouin. La face que tu me fais me donne la joie et le bonheur d'être avec toi. Ça remplit mon coeur pour un mois d'amour et de plaisir. Toi et moi, on est comme des siamoises collées par la main. Pas moyen de nous séparer. Si quelqu'un nous sépare, mon coeur se brisera en mille miettes. Quand tu sors la langue, que tu plisses le front et que tu appuies sur ton nez, ça donne TA FACE DE BABOUIN !!

**Andréanne Tanguay, 10 ans, Lac-Beauport, QC
École Ste-Chrétienne**

Isn't it funny when people act like animals? One day
I was out strolling and
something was odd? All the
people were acting like
animals. That day I had arranged
to go down to the zoo, so down
I went. When I got to the
zoo there were no animals,
just people in cages. What was
going on? All of a sudden
I hear shouting, "Will, its your
turn!" I woke up! It was my
wife; it was my turn to go
in the animal charades. I
must have dozed off. It was
just a dream, or was it?

Barrett Taylor 13

Isn't it funny when people act like animals? One day, I was out strolling and something was odd. All the people were acting like animals. That day, I had arranged to go down to the zoo, so down I went. When I got there, there were no animals, just people in cages. What was going on? All of a sudden, I heard shouting, "Will, it's your turn!" I woke up! It was my wife; it was my turn to go in the animal charades. I must have dozed off. It was just a dream, or was it?

Barrett Taylor, Age 13, Davidson, SK
Davidson High School

Isn't it funny when penguins waddle? Do you ever wonder why? Once upon a time, when penguins walked normally, a group of them were walking through a cave, but a group of sleeping foxes blocked their way. Instead of asking them to move, they stepped on the foxes. This happened again with a sleeping polar bear and mammoth. When they reached the end of the cave, God appeared. He told them he saw the whole thing. God punished the penguins and others after them to waddle their whole life. That is why penguins waddle when they walk.

Jinny To, 13 years old

Isn't it funny when penguins waddle? Do you ever wonder why?
Once upon a time, when penguins walked normally, a group of
them were walking though a cave, but a group of sleeping foxes
blocked their way. Instead of asking them to move, they stepped
on the foxes. This happened again with a sleeping polar bear
and mammoth. When they reached the end of the cave, God
appeared. He told them he saw the whole thing. God punished
those penguins, and others after them, to waddle their whole life.
That is why penguins waddle when they walk.

Jinny To, Age 13, Burnaby, BC
Alpha Secondary School

199

Isn't it funny when . . .
Isn't it funny when your body does funny things? Like when your nose runs and your feet smell. I always thought your nose should smell and your feet should run. Could you imagine if you had a foot on your face and a nose on your feet? My eyes would go crossed when I try to tie my laces and I would have to bend over very far to blow my nose. Oh isn't it funny!

By Kailey Tomilin
7 years old

Isn't it funny when your body does funny things? Like when your nose runs and your feet smell. I always thought your nose should smell and your feet should run. Could you imagine if you had a foot on your face and a nose on your feet? My eyes would go crossed whenever I try and to tie my laces, and I would have to bend over very far to blow my nose. Oh, isn't it funny!

Kailey Tomilin, Age 7, Calgary, AB
McKenzie Lake School

Isn't it funny when a chicken makes a big deal of crossing the road. One year he was too scared to cross the road, because of his fear. One day he got lost at a corner, and his family worried about him so they went to find him anywhere. Finally, the chicken had to go home so he got the courage to cross the road. When the chicken arrived home noone was there. So he went looking for his family. He eventually found his family. He later became fearless of crossing the road. Eventually helping others cross the road too.

Nicco Torres age: 8

Isn't it funny when a chicken makes a big deal of crossing the road. One year, he was too scared to cross the road because of his fear. One day, he got lost at a corner, and his family worried about him so they went to find him anywhere. Finally, the chicken had to go home, so he got up courage to cross the road. When the chicken arrived home, no one was there. So he went looking for his family. He eventually found his family. He later became fearless of crossing the road, eventually helping others cross the road too.

Nicco Torres, Age 8, Hamilton, ON
St. Catherine of Siena School

Isn't it funny when my shoes walk away alone. One day I was looking for my shoes. I could not find them anywhere. I looked out the window and saw my shoes walking away alone. I ran after them. The faster I ran, the faster they ran. I could not catch up. After awhile I caught them. I asked them why they ran away. They said that they ran away because I did not clean them. I promised them that I would clean them from now on. So we went home.

Jennifer Tschetter, 11

Isn't it funny when my shoes walk away alone. One day, I was looking for my shoes. I could not find them anywhere. I looked out the window and saw my shoes walking away alone. I ran after them. The faster I ran, the faster they ran. I could not catch up. After a while, I caught them. I asked them why they ran away. They said that they ran away because I did not clean them. I promised them that I would clean them from now on. So we went home.

Jennifer Tschetter, Age 11, Fort Macleod, AB
Thompson Colony School

Isn't it funny when toys come to life. You're probably wondering what I am talking about, because everyone knows that toys are made of plastic and don't have a brain which can't possibly come to life. Well, this actually really happened to me! Just a week ago I went to the library and discovered this old dusty book about magic spells. I took the book back to my house and sat down on my bed in my room. I found a spell about toys, and within a minute all my toys ran around my room. That was so cool. Freaky!

Hannah Tulloch, age: 12

Isn't it funny when toys come to life. You're probably wondering what I am talking about, because everyone knows that toys are made of plastic and don't have brains, which can't possibly come to life. Well, this actually really happened to me! Just a week ago, I went to the library and discovered this old dusty book about magic spells. I tool the book back to my house and sat down on my bed in my room. I found a spell about toys, and within a minute, all my toys ran around my room. That was so cool. Freaky!

Hannah Tulloch, Age 12, Blind River, ON
Blind River Public School

203

Que c'est drôle quand badaboum l'éléphant appris à faire des bulles. Le jour de
son anniversaire, quand badaboum se
réveilla, il était enrhumé. Il décida
donc d'aller se promener. En se
baladant, il vit une motte gluante
rose. Il le prit et le mâcha. Il se dit :
miam ! mais tout en mâchant sa
gomme, son nez commença à piquer.
Il s'écria : "atchoum", une bulle sortie
et l'enveloppa. Il s'envola dans les airs
et oups ! il se cogna contre l'écorce d'un
grand arbre. Sa bulle éclata. Il atterrit
dans sa cour. Tout le monde s'écria :
surprise ! avec un gâteau aux
gommes.

Andréa Turcotte   10 ans

Que c'est drôle quand Badaboum l'éléphant
appris à faire des bulles. Le jour de son
anniversaire, quand Badaboum se réveilla,
il était enrhumé. Il décida donc d'aller se
promener. En se baladant, il vit une motte
gluante rose. Il la prit et la mâcha. Il se dit: miam ! mais tout
en mâchant sa gomme, son nez commenca à piquer. Il s'écria :
« atchoum », une bulle sortie et l'enveloppa. Il s'envola dans
les airs et oups ! Il se cogna contre l'écorce d'un grand arbre.
Sa bulle éclata. Il atterrit dans sa cour. Tout le monde s'écria :
« surprise ! » avec un gâteau aux gommes.

Andréa Turcotte, 10 ans, St-Hyacinthe, QC
École Douville

Que c'est drôle quand l'hiver arrive.
Les flocons se glissants doucement
au sol, le givre recouvrant les vitres
geleés et par dessus tout, le beau
paysage blanc s'étendant sur l'horizon.
En hiver, tout le monde s'amusent à
faire des boules de neige, à faire des
plein de sports comme du ski, du patin
et même de la luge. En décembre, les
maisons sont couvertes de milliers
de lumières et de décorations qui
l'illuminent la ville de jolie étincelles
afin de célébrer l'arrivé de Noël! Cette
merveilleuse saison, nous apportes plein
de choses drôles et amusantes à
découvrirent. C'est à vous de les trouvés!

Sheila turgeon-hébert   13ans

Que c'est drôle quand l'hiver arrive. Les flocons se glissant doucement au sol, le givre recouvrant les vitres gelées et par-dessus tout, le beau paysage blanc s'étendant sur l'horizon. En hiver, tout le monde s'amuse à faire des bagarres de boules de neige, à faire plein de sports comme du ski, du patin et même de la luge ! En décembre, les maisons sont couvertes de milliers de lumières et de décorations qui illuminent la ville afin de célébrer l'arrivée de Noël ! Cette merveilleuse saison nous apporte plein de choses drôles et amusantes à découvrir. C'est à vous de les trouver !

Sheila Turgeon-Hébert, 13 ans, Laval, QC
Poly-jeunesse

Isn't it funny when you're wading in the warm cove waters
of the ocean with the sand curling around your toes, and you feel
nibbles. Could it be the tentacles of a vicious jellyfish about
to sting, or perhaps it is the hairy fronds of seaweed wrapping
about your legs, or worse yet, the snap of the black mussel.
You dangle your fingers into the warm water, and your hand
digs into the slimy, slippery muck. Then, scooping up, a bevy
of delightful, miniature lobsters surface, their pincers clutching
at the air.

Tara Joy Ubbens, Age 13, Toronto, ON
Timothy Christian School

Que c'est drôle quand tu essais d'être sérieux. Tes petits yeux pétillants s'efforçant de se plisser, ta bouche prennant une forme inhabituelle chez toi, le nez douloureusement retroussé, des rides sillonnant difficilement ton front lisse et les coins de tes joues, qui donnent l'air d'avoir été attachées avec du papier collant, veulent se fendre en sourire jusqu'à tes oreilles. Heureusement que tu n'es qu'un petit garçon de dix ans, tu auras suffisament de temps pour perfectionner ton air sérieux. Par pitié, maintenant, regagne ton sourire d'enfant émerveillé par la vie, sinon je vais bien finir par mourrir d'un rire incontrôlable.

Elise Veillette   12 ans

Que c'est drôle quand tu essaies d'être sérieux. Tes petits yeux pétillants s'efforçant de se plisser, ta bouche prenant une forme inhabituelle chez toi, le nez douloureusement retroussé, des rides sillonnant difficilement ton front lisse et les coins de tes joues, qui donnent l'air d'avoir été attachées avec du papier collant, veulent se fendre en sourire jusqu'à tes oreilles. Heureusement que tu n'es qu'un petit garçon de dix ans, tu auras suffisamment de temps pour perfectionner ton air sérieux. Par pitié, maintenant, regagne ton sourire d'enfant émerveillé par la vie, sinon je vais bien finir par mourir d'un rire incontrôlable.

Elise Veillette, 12 ans, Mirabel, QC
Académie Ste-Thérèse

Isn't it funny when your imagination soars, and suddenly your bath water turns into the vast, open ocean and you're the captain of a small sailboat, teetering and tottering! You see a great whale breaching into the air, making large waves; up and down you rock... and the whale is nothing more than a rubber duck! Isn't it funny when the bath bubbles turn into Mount Everest? You are skiing down the face of the mountain with an avalanche pursuing your every move... and the avalanche is no more than you blowing the bubbles from your knees... Isn't it funny...?

Jordan Venoit, 12

Isn't it funny when your imagination soars, and suddenly, your bath water turns into the vast open ocean and you're the captain of a small sailboat, teetering and tottering! You see a great whale breaching into the air, making large waves; up and down you rock... and the whale is nothing more than a rubber duck! Isn't it funny when the bath bubbles turn into Mount Everest? You are skiing down the face of the mountain with an avalanche pursuing your every move... and the avalanche is no more than you blowing the bubbles from your knees... Isn't it funny...?

Jordan Venoit, Age 12, Shawnigan Lake, BC
George Bonner School

Isn't it funny when you Catch a fish and it does a back flip. Then you see a whale and it does a back flip, then you see two more fish that do a somersault. So if you see a fish watch for a back flip.

Collin Viner 7

Isn't it funny when you catch a fish and it does a back flip. Then, you see a whale and it does a back flip; then you see two more fish that do a somersault. So, if you see a fish, watch for a back flip.

Collin Viner, Age 7, Ottawa, ON
Severn Avenue Public School

Isn't it funny when rhinos charge
something by mistake? One day Rhino was
lumbering through the grasslands when he
spied a pond. He charged, head lowered
ready to drink, but instead of drinking he
bounced into the air and landed on his
tail! The pond was a blue trampoline
hidden in the grass! Rhino burned with anger.
He howled with such force he flipped
backward! Seething, he bucked.
Unfortunately, he bucked with such
strength that dirt flew up his nose!
Embarrassed, Rhino fopped down to ponder
his actions. "From now on, I will think
before I act," Rhino thought.

Perrin Waldock, age 7

Isn't it funny when rhinos charge something by mistake?
One day, Rhino was lumbering through the grasslands when
he spied a pond. He charged, head lowered, ready to drink,
but instead of drinking, he bounced into the air and landed
on his tail! The pond was a blue trampoline hidden in the grass!
Rhino burned with anger. He howled with such force, he flipped
backward! Seething, he bucked. Unfortunately, he bucked with
such strength that dirt flew up his nose! Embarrassed, Rhino
flopped down to ponder his actions. "From now on, I will think
before I act," Rhino thought.

Perrin Waldock, Age 7, Chilliwack, BC
Nechako ebus School

Isn't it funny when a chicken quacks? Isn't it funny when a mouse chases a cat? Isn't it funny when a hippo dances in a swimsuit? It all started on Sunday night when the sun didn't go down. The animals noticed, so everything went wrong that day. The cats and dogs played all day. Foxes and deers love each other. Suddenly, a bright light appeared at evening time and said, "Remember!" Then it disappeared. The next day everything went back to normal. Anyway, after that I lived happily ever after. The End!

Crystal Wang, age: 9

Isn't it funny when a chicken quacks? Isn't it funny when a mouse chases a cat? Isn't it funny when a hippo dances in a swimsuit? It all started on Sunday night, when the sun didn't go down. The animals noticed, so everything went wrong that day. The cats and dogs played all day. Foxes and deers love each other. Suddenly, a bright light appeared at evening time and said, "Remember!" Then it disappeared. The next day, everything went back to normal. Anyway, after that, I lived happily ever after. The end!

Crystal Wang, Age 9, Coquitlam, BC
École Porter Street Elementary

Isn't it funny when you think that there are thousands of rocks in the world that are getting thrown in the water at this very moment? The rocks that you pick up to throw in the water have probably already been touched by people who, if they were still alive, would be hundreds of years old by now. Just remember, next time you go to throw a rock in the water, you are not the first person to touch it! Could Cleopatra have touched that rock when she was a kid? You just never know.

Paige Wergeland, age 8

Isn't it funny when you think that there are thousands of rocks in the world that are getting thrown in the water at this very moment? The rocks that you pick up to throw in the water have probably already been touched by people who, if they were still alive, would be hundreds of years old by now. Just remember, next time you go to throw a rock in the water, you are not the first person to touch it! Could Cleopatra have touched that rock when she was a kid? You just never know.

Paige Wergeland, Age 8, Victoria, BC
St. Michaels School

Isn't it funny when you see a flying penguin? Of course it is, because penguins don't fly, except one penguin named George. One day, George found a magical four leaf clover. Suddenly the clover said "I'll give you one wish." "I wish I could fly" said George. "You may fly for two hours," replied the clover. Up, up went George. The other penguins were jealous. They spotted a plane and asked the pilot for a ride. As they went up, George came down, because his time was up. And that my friends, is the story of George the flying penguin.

Alexandra White age 10

Isn't it funny when you see a flying penguin? Of course it is, because penguins don't fly, except one penguin named George. One day, George found a magical four leaf clover. Suddenly, the clover said, "I'll give you one wish." "I wish I could fly," said George. "You may fly for two hours," replied the clover. Up, up went George. The other penguins were jealous. They spotted a plane, and asked the pilot for a ride. As they went up, George came down because his time was up. And that, my friends is the story of George, the flying penguin.

Alexandra White, Age 10, Hamilton, ON
Earl Kitchner School

Isn't it funny when you meet your exact clone? One day, I bumped into a girl my age. She looked familiar. I asked for her name. She said "Deanne". The name was familiar too. When I got home, I searched for her face in my photos. I had no luck. As I was brushing my teeth, I realized that the girl looked like me! She walked, talked, and was named like me! She was my clone! Then I thought maybe everyone has a clone. Maybe, someday, you will meet your clone too.

THE END!

Deanna Whitney, age 11

Isn't it funny when you meet your exact clone? One day, I was walking down the street. I bumped into a girl my age. She looked familiar. I asked for her name. She said "Deanne". The name was familiar too. When I got home, I searched for her face in my photos. I had no luck. As I was brushing my teeth, I realized that the girl looked like me! She walked, talked, and was named like me! She was my clone! Then I thought, maybe everyone has a clone. Maybe, someday, you will meet your clone too. The End.

Deanna Whitney, Age 11, Dartmouth, NS
Humber Park Elementary School

Isn't it funny when you go to bed as a guy and you wake up as a girl? I looked around and saw barbies, boy rockstar pictures, stuffed animals, and everything was pink! I had these weird pajamas on which I took off, and my chest looked way different than the night before! Then the phone was ringing and some nosy girl wanted to know what I was wearing to school. Like I knew! After I spent hours figuring out what to paint and what to pluck my alarm went off and took me out of this terrible nightmare!

Bradley Wierenga Age 13

Isn't it funny when you go to bed as a guy and you wake up as a girl? I looked around and saw Barbies, boy rock star pictures, stuffed animals, and everything was pink! I had these weird pajamas on, which I took off, and my chest looked way different than the night before! Then, the phone was ringing and some nosy girl wanted to know what I was wearing to school. Like I knew! After I spent hours figuring out what to paint and what to pluck, my alarm went off and took me out of this terrible nightmare!

Bradley Wierenga, Age 13, Woodstock, ON
Harris Heights Public School

Isn't it funny when a cow jumped over the moon. I'll tell you about the story of the cow. Ever since he was a kid he was special. Everybody thought so. But there was one problem he couldn't see or jump. He tried and tried but he couldn't jump or see. So when he was walking through a forest he heard a glowing sound behind a tree and went to see what it was. It was a cape. He tried it on and he could fly and jump high and could see. He was Super Cow who jumped over the moon.

Matthew Wiggins, 10

Isn't it funny when a cow jumped over the moon. I'll tell you the story of the cow. Ever since he was a kid, he was special. Everybody thought so. But there was one problem, he couldn't see or jump. He tried and tried but he couldn't jump or see. So, when he was walking through a forest, he heard a glowing sound behind a tree and went to see what it was. It was a cape. He tried it on and he could fly, and jump high, and could see. He was Super Cow, who jumped over the moon.

Matthew Wiggins, Age 10, Edmonton, AB
Belmead Elementary School

Isn't it funny when during wintertime, you're just around the corner from your friend, with the most round, white, fluffy, packed and perfect snowball in your hands. All of the sudden you hear her light footsteps getting closer and closer. You're ready to aim then, "Boom!" And there is the second most perfect snowball in your face courtesy of... your friend!

Kelly Ann Wilson 12

Isn't it funny when, during winter time, you're just around the corner from your friend, with the most round, white, fluffy, packed and perfect snowball in your hands. All of a sudden, you hear her light footsteps getting closer and closer. You're ready to aim, then, "BOOM", and there is the second most perfect snowball in your face, courtesy of... your friend.

Kelly Ann Wilson, Age 12, Woodlawn, ON
Fitzroy Centennial School

Isn't it funny when you think everything is going well, but then things take a turn for the worse? My owner, Julia, saved me from a sunglass rack in Winnipeg and brought me back to her home in Toronto. Next thing I know, we're kayaking at her cottage when she loses her balance and SPLASH! - forgets I'm on her head! In I went, not knowing where I was. I was scared. Tons of fish swam past me. I didn't even know if anyone was actually looking for me! I lost hope until fingers clenched around me. Yeah! Julia saved me!

Julia Wilton, age 10

Isn't it funny when you think everything is going well, but then things take turn for the worse? My owner, Julia, saved me from a sunglass rack in Winnipeg, and brought me back to her home in Toronto. Next thing I know, we're kayaking at her cottage, when she loses her balance and SPLASH!... forgets I'm on her head! In I went, not knowing where I was. I was scared. Tons of fish swam past me. I didn't even know if anyone was actually looking for me! I lost hope until fingers clenched around me. Yeah! Julia saved me.

Julia Wilton, Age 10, Toronto, ON
Trafalgar Castle School

Isn't it funny when you lose a tooth and
your tongue always wants to feel the gap
where your tooth was. Your mouth feels
empty without the tooth and when the
tooth has grown back your mouth feels
nice again. When you loose the two
front teeth you look like a jack-o-lantern.
I hate it when you loose a tooth and
people tease you. I like it when your
teeth are all grown back.

Sara. a. Wipf, 9

Isn't it funny when you lose a tooth and your tongue always
wants to feel the gap where your tooth was. Your mouth feels
empty without the tooth and when the tooth has grown back,
your mouth feels nice again. When you lose the two front
teeth, you look like a jack-o-lantern. I hate it when you lose
a tooth and people tease you. I like it when your teeth
are all grown back.

Sara. A. Wipf, Age 9, Botha, AB
Lone Pine Colony School

Isn't it funny when storks bring babies
to your doorstep? I know a
chickadee named Bob. Bob's friends
convinced him he was a stork. Since
then, he's been attempting to bring
babies to their rightful "owners."
But of course, he gets the big
kid shift and he takes the plump
babies to his or her parents. Bob
was a successful little bird, but he
wanted to win Employee of the
Month so badly. One day Bob's
carrying had paid off. His boss
approached him and told Bob he
was Employee of the Month! Bob's
very happy now, and very retired.

Kayla Wojcik, 11

Isn't it funny when storks bring babies to your doorstep?
I know a chickadee named Bob. Bob's friends convinced
him he was a stork. Since then, he's been attempting to bring
babies to their rightful 'owners'. But of course, he gets the
big-kid shift, and he takes the plump babies to his or her
parents. Bob was a successful little bird, but he wanted
to win Employee Of The Month so badly. One day, Bob's
carrying had paid off. His boss approached him and told Bob
he was Employee Of The Month! Bob's very happy now,
and very retired.

Kayla Wojcik, Age 11, Burlington, ON
Orchard Park Public School

Isn't it funny when animals act like humans? I had a dream
that all the animals around the world suddenly acted and lived
like humans. Chimpanzees that worked in offices, wearing suits
and talking on telephones. Dolphins teaching other animals to
swim. Giraffes as librarians; their long necks would be useful
in finding books on high shelves. Owls as scientists, dogs as
teachers, peacocks as models, and the list goes on. So, what
about the humans? Human beings would be locked up in
cages to be displayed. But would this be an amusing dream,
or a nightmare?

Michael Wong, Age 13, Scarborough, ON
Terry Fox Public School

221

Isn't it funny when it snows in July? Snowmen appear on beaches where sandcastles used to be. Dad puts away the lawn mower and gets out his snow shovel. Children toboggan down the ramp instead of skateboarding. Classes cancel their trips to the beach and go skiing. One day I am in my swimsuit, and the next day I am in my snowpants. Sometimes it is so confusing. I look at my calendar upside down. Is it summer or winter or a new season called "sumter"? It doesn't matter to me as long as I have my summer vacation!

Shannon Wong, 7 years 9 months

Isn't it funny when it snows in July? Snowmen appear on beaches where sandcastles used to be. Dad puts away the lawn mower and gets out his snow shovel. Children toboggan down the ramp instead of skateboarding. Classes cancel their trips to the beach and go skiing. One day, I am in my swimsuit, and the next, I am in my snow pants. Sometimes it is so confusing. I look at my calendar upside down. Is it summer or winter, or a new season called 'sumter'? It doesn't matter to me, as long as I have my summer vacation!

Shannon Wong, Age 7, Richmond Hill, ON
Academy for Gifted Children

Isn't it funny when you are able to talk to animals. Because, every day in life, you would see animals and then that's when the talking comes in! So, that means every day you can say "hi" to an animal. And, then, think of the possibilities. When you and your friends are playing hide-and-go-seek, your pets at home could have a lab somewhere, and track them, and have a little speaker to talk to them. And, every game, you would win! If you could talk to animals, life would be easier.

Brittany W. Woodhall, Age 9, Kitchener, ON
Brigadoon Public School

Isn't it funny when your spoon talks to you? One day, Lucie and Frank decided to collect spoons. The one thing they didn't know was they had the magical spoon. Frank was telling Lucie that it would be funny if spoons could talk. The next day, when they came home, Lucie and Frank counted their spoons and heard someone say, "ow". Lucie found the magical spoon, and it wouldn't stop talking to her. It told her she was mean, and should let spoons be free. Frank told the spoon that spoons were for eating with. The spoon screamed and ran.

Leanne M. Woodward, Age 11

Isn't it funny when your spoon talks to you? One day, Lucie and Frank decided to collect spoons. The one thing they didn't know was they had the magical spoon. Frank was telling Lucie that it would be funny if spoons could talk. The next day, when they came home, Lucie and Frank counted their spoons and heard someone say, "ow". Lucie found the magical spoon, and it wouldn't stop talking to her. It told her she was mean, and should let spoons be free. Frank told the spoon that spoons were for eating with. The spoon screamed and ran.

Leanne M. Woodward, Age 11, Niagara Falls, ON
Princess Margaret School

Isn't it funny when people misunderstand you, like the other
day, when my mom asked me to wash the bathrooms and
I washed the mushrooms. When I was at my Grandpa's
house, he asked me to turn off the light and I thought
he said "do you want to fight?" The other day, the teacher
asked me to stay after school, and I thought she said to
jump in the pool. When my Dad asked me to go to bed,
I thought he said to soak my head. Isn't that funny.

Matthew Wright, Age 9, Windsor, ON
Northwood School

Isn't it fun when you fall down with the waves as you feel the cool prick of the ocean breeze. The waves lap against you. The strength of the water is as strong as a hurricane but as soft as a warm blanket. The sound of the waves is as soothing as purring kittens. Even the waves lap against the shore at an even tempo as if it is a clock with the sounds of time. In the sun the waves cast their glittering light like a thousand diamonds floating in the water. That was my day at the beach.

cassie young age 9

Isn't it funny when you fall down with the waves as you feel the cool prick of the ocean breeze. The waves lap against you. The strength of the water is as strong as a hurricane, but as soft as a warm blanket. The sound of the waves is as soothing as purring kittens; even the waves lap against the shore at an even tempo as if it is a clock with the sounds of time. In the sun, the waves cast their glittering light like a thousand diamonds floating in the water. That was my day at the beach.

Cassie Young, Age 9, Hanmer, ON
Redwood Acres Public School

Isn't it funny, when you see something but it's not there. Like a mirage, you see it, but it's not really there. I'm a child without sight. One night I had a dream. I imagined sailing through the ocean, watching dolphins swimming by. I opened my eyes, nothing appeared, so I closed my eyes. I pictured a rainbow sparkling after the rain. I opened my eyes, nothing. I slowly. Shut my eyes. I saw my mom. She gave me a hug. I opened my eyes, and for a second it felt like I could see!

Destiny Young, 9

Isn't it funny when you see something, but it's not there. Like a mirage, you see it, but it's not really there. I'm a child without sight. One night I had a dream. I imagined sailing through the ocean, watching dolphins swimming by. I opened my eyes; nothing appeared, so I closed my eyes. I pictured a rainbow sparkling after the rain. I opened my eyes, nothing. I slowly shut my eyes. I saw my mom. She gave me a hug. I opened my eyes, and for a second, it felt like I could see.

Destiny Young, Age 9, Thorndale, ON
St. Joseph French Immersion

Isn't it funny when you watch the little kids playing, running freely with no worries what so ever. To think that I was once one of them, how impatient I was to grow up, to finally do what I want to do, be whom I want to be, away from the reach of parents. Now being twelve, I'm free to roam and explore the path ahead. Little did I know before, there's also obstacles and challenges waiting. Feeling scared, I wish I was young again, but too late for that. " I couldn't wait to grow up, but now I have to. "

May Zhang, 12

Isn't it funny when you watch the little kids playing, running freely with no worries whatsoever. To think that I was once one of them, how impatient I was to grow up. To finally do what I want to do, be who I want to be, away from the reach of parents. Now, being twelve, I'm free to roam and explore the path ahead. Little did I know before, there's also obstacles and challenges waiting. Feeling scared, I wish I was young again, but too late for that. "I couldn't wait to grow up, now I have to."

May Zhang, Age 12, Mississauga, ON
Camilla Public School

Isn't it funny when people say, "Many hands make light work," but it seems that when you're in groups, everybody argues? Here's a story about animals that worked together to survive. Long ago, a cheetah, a fox, and an ox were stranded on a forgotten island. Together, they worked to find food. Cheetah, the fastest, ran around the island to search for food. Fox, the smartest, thought of ways to carry it. And ox, the strongest, used the inventions to carry the food to their shelter. Using this system, they lived for many years until they were rescued.

Connie Zhao, Age 10, Toronto, ON
Summit Heights School

RoseMarie Condon

RoseMarie Condon was born in Toronto. The Beach District where she grew up was a wonderful place to explore and sketch and learn about the natural world.

As an illustrator and designer, RoseMarie has created many children's books, toys, games and pastimes for multi-national corporations. She works in all traditional media as well as illustrating on her computer to create whimsical or humorous characters that sometimes inspire her to write stories or poems about them. Her two cats, Jazz Purr and Tiger Lily help out in her studio.

RoseMarie has just finished designing and illustrating five whimsical, animated Christmas windows for the Hudson's Bay Company. They will appear in downtown Toronto and Vancouver in December 2003.

As a fine artist RoseMarie paints in oil, acrylic and watercolour. Traveling extensively throughout Canada and the high Arctic, she has sketched, painted and gathered reference material for her paintings. In a realistic style, she paints heritage homes, landscapes, floral, figurative and animal subjects. Quite a number of her paintings have been reproduced in limited editions.

To see more of RoseMarie's work, visit www.rosemariecondon.com

RoseMarie is a member of the Arts and Letters Club of Toronto and Visual Arts Ontario.

Illustratrice/Dessinatrice

RoseMarie Condon est née à Toronto. Le quartier « Beaches » où elle a grandi était une place merveilleuse pour explorer, esquisser et apprendre sur le monde naturel.

En tant qu'illustratrice et dessinatrice, RoseMarie a créé plusieurs livres pour enfants, des jouets, des jeux et des passe-temps pour plusieurs compagnies multinationales. Elle travaille dans tous les médias traditionnels et elle fait aussi des illustrations sur son ordinateur en créant des caractères fantaisistes ou comiques qui l'inspirent parfois à écrire des histoires ou des poèmes. Ses deux chats « Jazz Purr » et « Tiger Lily » l'aident dans son studio.

RoseMarie vient de terminer de dessiner et d'illustrer 5 vitrines de Noël pour la compagnie La Baie avec des caractères fantaisistes et animés. Elles seront dans les magasins La Baie du centre-ville de Toronto et de Vancouver en décembre 2003.

En tant qu'artiste raffinée, RoseMarie peint à l'huile, à l'acrylique et des aquarelles. En raison de ses fréquents voyages dans tout le Canada et dans la région arctique, elle a fait des esquisses, a peint et a recueilli du matériel de référence pour ses tableaux. Dans un style réaliste, elle peint des maisons protégées, des paysages, des sujets floraux, figuratifs et animaux. Un grand nombre de ses peintures ont été reproduites en éditions limitées.

Pour en connaître davantage au sujet des œuvres de RoseMarie, visitez le site www.rosemariecondon.com

RoseMarie est membre du Arts and Letters Club of Toronto et de Visual Arts Ontario.